D1288670

DIRECTORY OF MARYLAND PHOTOGRAPHERS 1839 - 1900

Ross J. Kelbaugh

HISTORIC GRAPHICS
BALTIMORE, MARYLAND

HISTORIC GRAPHICS
7023 Deerfield Rd.
Baltimore, MD 21208

FIRST EDITION 1988

ISBN 0-914931-00-8
Library of Congress Catalog Card Number 88-82285

Printed in the United States of America

CONTENTS

ACKNOWLEDGEMENTS

Over the years, many people have contributed their time and resources to help make this project possible. I would like to thank the following: Gil Barrett for his success in uncovering examples of the work of previously unknown Maryland photographers; Erik Davis for sharing his research on the Bendann brothers; Richard Flint, the Peale Museum, for his suggestions concerning research sources; Tom Gordon, Jr. for making available images and related photographica as well as the portrait of H. B. Grammer; Michael Isekoff, William McIntosh, and Beverly and Jack Wilgus for sharing their collections of Maryland photography; Howard Manis for providing material on Jesse Whitehurst; Donna and Vincent Sunderdick for their research on Maryland photographic patents; Gail Zlotowitz for her interest and encouragement as well as her many dawn expeditions to local flea markets which uncovered numerous examples of work of Maryland photographers.

Several individuals have been particularly instrumental in helping to bring this project to fruition. I would first like to thank Henry Deeks, photographic dealer and historian, whose professional and personal contributions were immeasurable. Earl J. Coates has given invaluable advice and counsel throughout this project. Mr. Coates has set the standard for the true researcher and served as an inspiration for my efforts. David Ashton and Daniel Toomey contributed their expertise in book design and production. Jeffrey Schultz helped to make the management of this information a much easier process. Sue Tustin provided editorial assistance as well. Lastly, I would like to thank Nancy B. Frye for her support and understanding through the many phases of this project.

PREFACE

In 1989, the 150th anniversary of the introduction of photography will be marked by the world as mankind continues to appreciate the impact of this momentous invention. Over the past decade, those who practiced this medium professionally during the nineteenth century in the United States have been catalogued as part of a project coordinated by Richard Rudisill, Curator of Photographic History at the Museum of New Mexico. This directory marks the first effort to compile the pioneers who contributed to this story in Maryland.

For many years, the study of nineteenth century photography in Maryland had been neglected. Recently, numerous photographically illustrated books have brought to the public a glimpse of the people and times long since past in our state's history. Now, it is fitting that the people who helped to make these images possible have themselves received the same attention. It is hoped that this publication will be a resource for those who have the responsibility and interest in interpreting the visual records of our past. It is also hoped that others will share information about these people so that these pieces of our state's photographic puzzle may be further supplemented.

From the earliest days of the daguerreotype, Maryland has played a major role in fostering the growth of the photographic medium in our country. Baltimore, the state's center of industry and commerce, emerged early as the local center for photography — a position that it held until well into the twentieth century. In addition, other urban areas proved to be fertile soil for the new medium to take root. By the end of the 1800's, over 750 people had been involved in this story which provided the Free State with its rich photographic legacy. It is to these men and women that this directory is dedicated.

Ross J. Kelbaugh
Baltimore, Maryland

DIRECTORY KEY

AC	Author's Collection
AD	Floyd and Marion Rinhart, *The American Daguerreotype* (Athens, Georgia: University of Georgia Press, 1981)
AS	*American Sentinel* (Westminster, Carroll Co.)
BA	Baltimore *American and Commercial Daily Advertiser*
BC	*The Biographical Cyclopedia of Representative Men of Maryland and District of Columbia* (Baltimore: National Publishing Co., 1879)
BCU	*The Union* (Towson, Baltimore County)
BD	Business directories for the years cited
CD	City directories for the years cited
CDV	Carte de visite
DA	Beaumont Newhall, *The Daguerreotype in America* (New York: Duell, Sloan, & Pearce, 1961)
DC	R. G. Dun Collection, Baker Library, Harvard University Graduate School of Business Administration
HCP	*A Half Century's Progress of the City of Baltimore* (New York: International Publishing Co., 1886)
IM	*Industries of Maryland* (Baltimore: Historical Publishing Co, 1882)
ITA	Solomon N. Carvalho, *Incidents of Travel and Adventure in the Far West* (New York: Derby & Jackson, 1857)
MID	John F. Porter, *Maryland and its Industrial Developments,* 1880
MHS	Maryland Historical Society Collection
PA	William Welling, *Photography in America: The Formative Years 1839-1900* (New York: Thomas Y. Crowell Co., 1978)
PC	Private Collection
PF	Richard Walzl, *The Photographer's Friend*, Volume I-IV, 1871-1874
PFAJ	*The Photographic and Fine Art Journal*, New York, 1854-1860
PP	*The Philadelphia Photographer*, Philadelphia, Pa., 1864-1888
PM	*Two Hundred and Fifty Years of Painting in Maryland* (Baltimore: Baltimore Museum of Art, 1945)
PR	United States Patent Records
PV	Louis Ginsberg, *Photographers in Virginia, 1839-1900* (Petersburg, Va.: Louis Ginsberg, 1986)
SD	State directories for the years cited
TS	*The Sun* (Baltimore)
USC	United States Census for the years cited
USMC	United States Census of Manufacturing and Agriculture for the years cited

DIRECTORY INTRODUCTION

The following directory represents a compilation of the photographers and those in closely related fields who were documented to have worked in Maryland within the time frame of this study. Baltimore's photographic establishments are listed through 1904, the year the Great Fire destroyed the early photographic district. Those operating outside of the city are listed through 1900.

The specific dates assigned for studio locations are based on the documentation found. Any date preceded by circa (ca.) indicates an estimation of the period represented by the graphic source material. It is possible, in some instances, that the photographer began at a particular location before, or continued in operation sometime after, the years indicated. During the years of 1861 and 1862, there were no directories published for Baltimore City. A business directory was published for the years 1863-1864. It should also be noted that in 1887, the city streets were renumbered, and a new address after that date does not necessarily indicate a relocation of the business.

Source citations have been provided in an order paralleling the information as an aid to other researchers. Records identified by abbreviations are listed in the "Directory Key." In addition, any photographers of the same name, but in different locations at widely separated time periods, have been listed individually until further research confirms a relationship.

The building to the left of Gallagher's Mercantile College at 205 W. Baltimore Street was one of the most active gallery locations in town. John Plumbe, Solomon N. Carvalho, and Jesse Whitehurst were among its many occupants. Note the prominent skylight on the roof that naturally illuminated the studio. Author's collection

ACHESON, ALICE C., photographer.
861 N. Howard St. (1902). CD

ACME COPYING CO.
1155 E. Baltimore (1892); "Crayons, photographs enlarged and copied." CD.

ADDIS, __________, daguerreotypist.
Advertisement for gallery at Light & Baltimore on November 29, 1853. TS.

ADDIS, ROBERT W., daguerreotypist.
187 Baltimore (1855-1856). CD.

ADREON, T.K. & CO., dealer of photographic supplies.
1419 N. Charles (1899). CD.

ALLARD & CO., photographers.
731 W. Baltimore (1886-?). CD.

> Allard & Co. (Successors to F. Beck), Photographers, No. 731 West Baltimore Street.- This establishment was founded by Mr. F. Hohlweg in 1865, who conducted the same with eminent success until 1883, when he was succeeded by F. Beck. In 1886, Mr. Beck disposed of the interest to Allard & Co., who have successfully conducted a large business in Baltimore as photographers, and the superior merit of their work has firmly established them in general regard as artists of unquestioned ability. Mr. Allard's experience as a practical photographer covers a period of eight years, and it has made him an expert in every detail of his work. The parlors are models of elegance and completeness. They make pictures of all styles, copy and enlarge old portraits, and execute crayon, pastel, and oil paintings in the most artistic manner, and in the pose, natural expression, and finish of their pictures they are equaled by few and surpassed by none of their contemporaries in the city. Mr. Allard is a native of Baltimore. HCP.

ALLARD, CHARLES L., photographer.
1825 N. Broadway (1898). CD.

ALLER, DAVID, daguerreotypist.
221 N. Gay (1856-1857). CD.

AMERICAN VIEW CO. (THE)
288 N. Charles (1898-1904); Chas. T. Walter, prop. (1900-1904). CD.

AMOS, WILLIAM W., photographer.
SW. corner of Baltimore & Poppleton (1873); 290 Lexington (1875); 4 S. Poppleton (1877). CD.

ANDERSON, L.T., photographer.
472 W. Baltimore St. (1867-1869). CD.

ARMIGER, BENJ. W., photographer.
303 1/2 Falls Road (1894); 305 Falls Road (1895); 309 Falls Road (1896); 303 1/2 Falls Road, "Armiger & Shultz" (1897); 307 Falls Ave. (1898); "Armiger Bro's," 716 N. Wolfe (1899); 1030 Pennsylvania Ave. (1901); 402 1/2 3rd Ave. N. (1902-1904). CD.

ARNO, ___________, photographer.
28 E. Baltimore (ca. 1870). Imprint on cabinet card, AC.

ASHMANN, WILLIAM, photographer.
Born in Maryland, 1861; photographer for William Chase (ca. 1880); 17 W. Lexington (1889-1904). U.S.C. 1880, imprint on cabinet card, AC, CD.

AULD, H., daguerreotypist.
233 Baltimore (1849-1850). CD.

****

BACHRACH, DAVID, photographer.
Corner of Lexington and Eutaw (October 13, 1869-1885); and corner of Baltimore & Poppleton (1873-1874); 174 Lexington (1886-1887); and 327 W. Lexington (1887); 327 W. Lexington (1888-1904); and 329 W. Lexington (1894-1895). CD, TS, January 31, 1920.
(see biography)

BACHRACH, MOSE, photographer.
Born in Prussia, 1851; living in the 19th Ward. U.S.C. 1880.

BACON, JAMES F., daguerreotypist, ambrotypist.
472 W. Baltimore (1858-1860). CD.

BAER, LIZZIE, employed in a photograph gallery.
Born in Maryland, 1863; living in the 15th Ward. U.S.C. 1880.

BAITLETT, WILLIAM, photographer.
Born in Ireland, 1845; prisoner in the Maryland State Penitentiary. U.S.C. 1880.

BAKER, FREDERICK S., daguerreotypist.
23 Baltimore (August 1846-1856). TS, CD.

BAKER, S., daguerreotypist.
NW. corner Baltimore & Centre Market; dwelling 71 E. Lombard (1849-1850). CD.

BAKER, WILLIAM, daguerreotypist.
$2000 capital invested; 500 plates used; 2 male employees; $100 ave. monthly cost of labor; 5000 likenesses produced annually. U.S.M.C. 1850.

BALCH, WILLIAM E., photographer.
48 and 50 N. Charles (1871); 50 N. Charles (1872); "...from Mr. J. E. Balch (sic) of this city, we received some elegant specimens of his photography in cards and cabinet size. It is gratifying to see that Baltimore in fine productions is not behind any of the other great cities. Mr. Balch is a recent sojourner with us, hailing, we understand, from New York, and has fitted up a neat first-class gallery, with the flattering prospects before him of doing a good business. The rapidly increasing population of the city will no doubt appreciate an addition to the several first-class studios already in successful operation." CD, PF, January 1871.

BALTIMORE PHOTOGRAPHIC CO.
66 and 120 Lexington (1885-1886); 17 and 201 W. Lexington (1887); 588 N. Gay (1896-1899). CD.

BANGS, ALBERT, employed in a photography gallery.
Born in Maryland, 1864; living in the 18th Ward. U.S.C. 1880.

BARCLAY, JOSEPH H., daguerreotypist.
158 N. High (1856-1857). CD.

BARNES, CHAUNCEY, daguerreotypist.
163 Baltimore (1844); 217 W. Baltimore (1845). TS, CD.

BASFORD, JOHN T., daguerreotypist.
56 Pearl St. (1858-1859). CD.

BASSFORD, ___________, daguerreotypist.
Advertisement for gallery at 111 N. Howard in The Sun, June 27, 1854.

BASSFORD, JOHN T., photographer.
480 Lexington (1864); over 91 W. Baltimore (1867-1869). CD.

BAUMGARTEN, ADOLPHUS, photographer.
Born in Hanover, 1839; SW. corner of Baltimore and Exeter (1867-1871). CD, BD.

BAUMGARTEN, HENRY, photographer.
560 W. Baltimore (1864); 71 E. Baltimore (1867). CD.

Entrance for the Bendann's Gallery at 207 W. Baltimore Street. Note their shield and helmet trademark over the doorway. Private collection

BEACH, HENRY, photographer.
Born in Maryland, 1849; living in the 8th Ward. U.S.C. 1870.

BEACH, WILLIAM, photographer.
Born in Maryland, 1820; living in the 8th Ward. U.S.C. 1870.

BEACH, WILLIAM A., photographer.
163 N. Gay (ca. 1863). Imprint on carte de visite, AC.

BEACH, WILLIAM J., photographer.
220 Light (1871). BD.

BECK, FREDERICK G., photographer.
Born in Maryland, 1855; & Hohlweg, 531 W. Baltimore (ca. 1880); Beck only, (1884-1886); U.S.C. 1880, imprint on cabinet card, AC, CD.

BECK, GEORGE F., photographer.
327 S. Sharp (1885); 731 W. Baltimore (1886); CD.

BEECHER, J. GREGG, photographer.
204 N. Eutaw (1878-1880). CD.

BEIER, FREDERICK C., photographer.
644 W. Baltimore (1899); 1256 E. North Ave. (1902-1903). CD, SD.

BELL, ___________, daguerreotypist.
117 Baltimore & South (old stand of Shew & Marks); "Daguerreotypes on pure gold and silver"; TS, May 29, 1851.

BELL, HARRY S., photographer.
314 W. Lombard (1898). CD.

BELL, THOMAS S., photographer.
Born in Virginia, 1859; son of Harry S. Bell; living in the 6th Ward. U.S.C. 1880.

BELL, WILLIAM H., photographer.
Born in Virginia, 1833; living in the 7th Ward. U.S.C. 1870.

BELTZ, JOHN JR., photographer.
417 N. Washington (1887). CD.

BENDANN BROTHERS (David and Daniel), photographers.
205 W. Baltimore (1859-1860); 207 W. Baltimore (1864-1872). "...they do a pretty good business of their kind, but are under heavy expenses and not making much if anything at this time [August 17, 1866], are rather fast young men [and they] make money easily and spend it freely." CD, DC (Maryland, Vol. 10, p. 111). (see biography)

BENDANN, DANIEL, photographer.
26 N. Charles (1874-1879); 24 N. Charles (1881-1885); 181 W. Baltimore (1886); 28 E. Baltimore (1887-1889); 5 N. Charles (1897-1898). CD.

BENTLEY, WILLIAM H., photographer.
906 E. Baltimore (1897-1904). CD.

BERGEN, JOHN S., photographer.
Over 70 Lexington (1879). CD.

BERMAN, LEON, photographer.
904 E. Baltimore (1896). CD.

BERSCH, CARL, photographer.
Born in 1835; over 20 N. Charles (1880-1881); 84 1/2 W. Fayette (1882). U.S.C. 1880, CD.

BETZ, JOHN, JR., photographer.
Born in Maryland, 1856; over 9 1/2 W. Baltimore (1877); 113 N. Washington (1880-1883); 107 N. Washington (1884); 417 N. Washington (1887-1889); and 415 N. Washington (1893, 1895, 1899-1900); 415 N. Washington only (1894, 1896-1898, 1904). U.S.C. 1880, CD.

BIDDER, DIETRICH, photographer.
Born in Hanover, 1840; living in the 14th Ward. U.S.C. 1870.

BISHOP, MARY E., "in photograph gallery."
Born in Maryland, 1854; living in the 7th Ward. U.S.C. 1870.

BISHOP, OLIVIA L., "works in photograph gallery."
Born in Maryland, 1850; living in the 7th Ward. U.S.C. 1870.

BLESSING & KUHN, photographers.
46 N. Charles (1882-1886); and Co. 214 N. Charles (1887-1904); and Fenge (1886-1904). CD. (see Maryland Counties)

> Blessing & Co., Photographic and Portrait Gallery, No. 214 (old No. 46) North Charles Street.- The progress of photograph and portrait-painting is admirably illustrated by the large and valuable establishment of Messrs. Blessing & Co., which founded in 1880, has risen to a position of great prominence. The members of the firm are Messrs. J.P. Blessing and Henry Fenge, both possessing long and mature experience, and thorough masters of their important vocation. The premises occupied comprise the three upper floors of the four-story building at No. 214 Charles street. They are elegantly fitted up throughout, and appropriately divided into parlor, reception, toilet, and operating

rooms. In the department of photography, the latest and most improved processes are used, the manipulation is careful and skillful, and the highest possible results are always reached, the pictures being unsurpassed for brilliancy, beauty, and correctness of effect, and permanency. As portrait painters, Messrs. Blessing & Co. have produced many splendid specimens of artistic handiwork, and the universal opinion is that for delicacy of touch, truthfulness to nature, and that tone which adds in such large measure to the excellence of a portrait, their productions are unrivaled. Portraits are made in oil, pastel, and crayon, and particular attention is given to miniatures and water colors. The prices are unusually moderate, and all work is fully guaranteed. The members of the firm are among the most accomplished exponents of their art in the Union. HCP.

BOGGS, S., daguerreotypist.
255 Baltimore (1842). TS.

BOHSEN, H., photographer.
1710 Eastern Ave.; prop. of Berlin Art Studio (ca. 1880). Imprint on cabinet card, AC.

BOKEE (W.H.) & JUDLIN (A.F.), daguerreotypists.
217 Baltimore ("Late King's Daguerrian Gallery"). TS, August 24, 1850.

BOWERMAN, WILLIAM H., photographer.
65 W. Baltimore (1874-1875); 1 N. Gay (1880-1885); and Becker, copying, 605 E. Baltimore (1887-1888); and Badger (1889); 420 E. Baltimore (1894-1895). CD.

BOWIE, CHARLES W., photographer.
63 W. Baltimore (1871-1872); and Co. 103 W. Baltimore (1873); 9 1/2 W. Baltimore (1875); 71 E. Baltimore (1877-1878); 161 N. Gay (1879); 163 N. Gay (ca. 1880). CD, imprint on CDV, AC.

BOWIE, GEORGE, photographer.
174 N. Washington (1879). CD.

BRACKLAND, B., ambrotypist, photographer.
8 E. Pratt (1862-1864). Imprint on carte de viste, AC.

BRACKLAND, BENJAMIN, photographer.
18 W. Pratt (1871). BD.

BRACKLAND, BERNARD, photographer.
406 N. Gay (1875-1876); 376 Light (1878-1883). CD.

BRADY, JAMES, daguerreotypist, ambrotypist, photographer.
472 Baltimore (1854-1859); 412 W. Baltimore (1859-1860?); 159 W. Baltimore (1863-1864). BD, CD, TS, March 9, 1854.

BRADY'S BRANCH GALLERY, photographers.
73 W. Baltimore (ca. 1870). Imprint on tintype, AC.

BRANSON, P.A., photographer.
Over 59 S. Howard (1867-1868). CD.

BRIDGEMAN, W.F., photographer.
Over 42 N. Eutaw (1867-1868). CD.

BRIGGS, ISAAC, daguerreotypist.
Mentioned in his journal that chronicled his photographic activities in Central Maryland that he began the daguerrean art on April 15, 1848 under the instruction of Mr. Pollock of Baltimore. MHS. (see Henry Pollock).

BROADBENT & CAREY, daguerreotypists.
211 and 128 Baltimore (1849-1850). CD, BA.

BROOKE & JUDLIN, daguerreotypists.
$300 invested; 200 plates used; 2 male employees; $80 ave. monthly cost of labor; 2500 likenesses produced annually. U.S.M.C. 1850.

BROOKS, H. PRESTON, photographer.
66 Lexington (1884). CD.

BROOKS, LOUIS JR., photographer.
282 N. Gay (1867-1868). CD.

BROWN, G.O., photographer, employee in Richard Walzl's gallery.
267 W. Lexington (ca. 1865); editor of Richard Walzl's The Photographer's Friend and signed Walzl's photograph receipts as cashier (1870's-1880's). Imprint on stereoviews, PF, Walzl receipt, AC.

BROWN, GEORGE W.C., photographer.
1601 N. Eden (1898-1899). CD.

BROWN, HARRY M., photographer.
114 W. Lexington (1902-1903); 109 W. Lexington (1904). CD.

BROWN, J., daguerreotypist.
127 Baltimore (1858). CD.

BUFFHAM BROTHERS, photographers.
116 S. Broadway (1882-1886); 5 W. Lexington (1888-1889). CD.

BURKE, BERKHARDT, photographer.
Born in Maryland, 1860; living in the 15th Ward. U.S.C. 1880.

BUSEY, NORVAL, H., photographer.
Born in Virginia, 1844; Hallwig and Busey, 20 N. Charles (1870-1871); 46 N. Charles (1872); NW. corner Charles & Fayette (1873-1874); over 24 N. Charles (1885-1886); 112 N. Charles (1887-1890). CD. (see biography)

BUTLER & McPHERSON, daguerreotypists.
Advertisement for move from 117 Baltimore to 20 North St. TS, February 3, 1848.

BUTLER BROTHERS, photographers.
NW. corner Charles & Fayette (1868-1869). CD.

BUTLER, JOSEPH, photographer.
Born in Canada, 1844; living in the 13th Ward. U.S.C. 1870.

BUTLER, SAMUEL, photographer.
Born in Canada, 1843; living in the 13th Ward. U.S.C. 1870.

BUTLER, W.C., daguerreotypist.
"Butler's Daguerrian Rooms, Baltimore St. between Gay & Tripolett's alley." TS, October 1, 1846.

****

CAMPBELL, JOHN, daguerreotypist, ambrotypist.
Born in Ireland, 1827; $1000 value of personal property; 234 Lexington (1859-1860). U.S.C. 1850, CD.

CARTER, WILLARD, photographer.
647 W. Baltimore (1900). CD.

CARVALHO, DAVID, daguerreotypist.
27 N. Gay; dwelling 26 Holliday (1855-1856). CD.

CARVALHO, SOLOMON NUNES, artist, daguerreotypist.
Born in England, 1815, died May 21, 1897; 205 Baltimore (June 1, 1849-1850); 35 S. High (1856-1857); 81 N. Liberty (1858-1859); Carvalho returned to the city after participating in the 1853 expedition of John C. Fremont to the West to write his account of the adventure and resume portrait painting until 1860 when he moved to New York. TS, BD, ITR, U.S.C. 1860.

CASKEY, DAVID W., daguerreotypist.
72 Jefferson (1856-1857). CD.

View of the camp of William M. Chase (left) and David Bachrach (right) taken while on one of their photographic expeditions. Author's collection

CASSEDAY & CO., photographers.
66 Lexington & 20 N. Charles (1884). CD.

CAWALKS, N., daguerreotypist.
Born in England, 1786; living in the 9th Ward. U.S.C. 1850.

CENTRAL PHOTO STUDIO, photographers.
427 E. Baltimore (1894-1896). CD.

CHANDLEE, ELLIS, photographer.
704 W. North Ave. (1899). CD.

CHARLES STREET NEW PHOTO CO., photographers.
102 N. Charles (1899). CD.

CHASE, HOWARD L. photographer.
564 Mosher (1899). CD.

CHASE, WILLIAM MOODY, photographer, stereoview publisher.
Born in Bolton, Massachusetts, 1817; employed at the gallery of R.D. Ridgeley, corner Lexington & Eutaw (1867-1868); established photographic publishing house at the corner Lexington & Eutaw (1872-1888); 330 W. Lexington (1889-1890); continued business at his home 941 W. Franklin (1891-1894); died November 20/21, 1901 in Boston. CD, MHS. (see David Bachrach)

CLANTICE, JOSEPH, photographer.
Born in Maryland, 1841; living in the 7th Ward. U.S.C. 1880.

CLARK, EDWARD, photographer.
327 S. Bond (1903). CD.

CLARK, HENRY H., daguerreotypist, photographer.
Born in Connecticut, 1815; Baltimore St. (1855-1856); 23 W. Baltimore (1859-1860?); 147 E. Baltimore where he resided with William H. Weaver (1880-1885). U.S.C. 1880, CD. (see William H. Weaver)

CLARK, SAMUEL J., photographer.
Born in Maryland, 1848; living in the 14th Ward. U.S.C. 1880.

CLARKE, ___________ (MRS.), photographic colorist.
"Mrs. Clarke, ARTIST, 561 Druid Hill Avenue, Baltimore, colors all description of Photographs in Water Colors, Crayons, and Monochrome, in a brilliant and highly finished style, at moderate prices. Terms on application." PP, April 1881.

CLEMMENS, AUGUSTUS D. JR., photographer.
Over 465 W. Baltimore (1867-1868); over 73 W. Baltimore (1868-1869). CD.

CLINEDINST, BARNETT M., photographer.
66 Lexington (1880-1881); over 120 Lexington (1882); and Casseday & Co., 66 & 120 Lexington (1883); 20 N. Charles (1885-1886); 218 N. Charles (1887); 216 N. Charles (1888-1889). CD.

COLE & LOTHROP, photographers.
102 W. Baltimore (ca. 1866). Imprint on tintype. AC.

COLEMAN, JOSEPH, daguerreotypist.
107 Little Green (1860). CD.

COOK, JOHN W., photographer.
Over 125 W. Baltimore (1883-1885). CD.

COOKE, BEECKMAN, daguerreotypist.
Established a studio at 63 Baltimore by January 1854; formed a partnership with John H. Walzl during that year under the name of "Cooke & Walzl;" Walzl bought out the partnership after six months. TS, January 3, 1854, BC. (see John H. Walzl)

COOKE, WARREN E., "cabinet photographs and albums."
278 W. Baltimore (1864); & Green (1865-66); Cooke only, 57 N. Eutaw (1867-1871). Imprint on carte de visite, AC, CD, BD.

COOPER, MORRIS, photographer.
574 N. Gay (1899). CD.

CORITHERS, RODNEY, photographer.
Born in England, 1825; living in the 11th Ward. U.S.C. 1870.

COSS & BOTELER, photographers.
93 Baltimore (ca. 1862). Imprint on carte de visite, AC.

COSS, G.M. & CO., ambrotypists, photographers.
Over 65 W. Baltimore (1859-1860). CD.

COSS (GEORGE), LEACH (WILLIAM) & IRWIN (EDWARD), photographers, ambrotypists.
127 W. Baltimore (1859-1860); Coss & Leach, over 159 W. Baltimore (1864). CD.

COVER, WILLIAM L., photographer.
Born in Maryland, 1844; 560 W. Baltimore (1868-1886); 754 W. Baltimore (1887-1903). U.S.C. 1880, CD.

COVIER, W.F., photographer.
Born in Maryland, 1839; living in the 14th Ward. U.S.C. 1870.

COWARD, WILLIAM, daguerreotypist.
Secured as an assistant at J. Wistar Davis' Gallery (1847); 19 E. Baltimore (1853, 1855-1856). TS, February 14, 1847, CD.

COWELL, DANIEL T., daguerreotypist, photographer.
Former head operator at Whitehurst's Daguerrean Gallery employed by Palmer L. Perkins, 99 Baltimore (1856-?); Richmond, Va. (1860); New Haven, Conn. (1875). TS, PV, PP.

COX, V.I., photographer.
Over 42 N. Eutaw (1868-1869). CD.

COX & WARD, photographers.
56 N. Charles (1870-1881); W.A. Cox only (1875-1889); Madison Ave, Ext. (1889). CD.

CRIM, FRANK, photographer.
Born in Bremen, 1852; living in the 9th Ward. U.S.C. 1880.

CRONHARDT, HENRY & SON, photographers.
1421 E. Madison (1888). CD.

CROWTHER, RODNEY, photographer.
Over SE. corner Lexington and Howard (1868-1869); over SE. corner of Gay & Front (1870-1871). CD, BD.

CULPEPPER, DANIEL W., photographer.
93 Baltimore (ca. 1864); over 73 & 127 W. Baltimore (1867-1868). Imprint on carte de viste, AC, CD.

CUMMINS, JAMES S., photographer, photographic supplies.
48 N. Charles (1881-1883); 7 N. Charles (1884-1886); 5 N. Charles (1887); 106 N. Charles (1888-1890); 103 N. Charles (1892); 106 N. Charles (1893-1899); and 40 W. Lexington (1898-1899); Cummins Photo Stock CO. (1896-1898); Cummins Studio (1899); Walzl (Sidney)- Cummins, Photographers' supplies, 20 W. Lexington (1900-1904). CD. (see Sidney Walzl)

> Jas. S. Cummins, Photographic Studio, No. 5 North Charles Street.- The photographic art has attained a perfection during the last twenty years little dreamed of in the days of Daguerre. The achievements of the leading artists of the present day are subjects of admiration and comment from an appreciative audience. The name Cummins will in this connection be inseparably identified with a large measure of success in Baltimore as the leading artist photographer in the city. His photographic studio is centrally located at No. 5 North Charles street. The reception rooms, parlors, and studio are elegant, spacious, and attractive, and are embellished with many fine works of art from the camera, brush, or pencil of Mr. Cummins. The excellence of these pictures, and their fidelity to every detail, and the true conception of the artist's mission, place
> (continued)

Mr. Cummins in the front rank of the profession. The light, accessories, and all the appliances necessary for a first-class establishment are perfect, and cannot fail to attract the attention and admiration of the cultivated classes of society, who constitute its principal patrons. Photography in all its branches is here executed, and the best and finest class of work is promptly produced. Pictures are taken by the instantaneous process, and thus patrons are enabled to obtain accurate and perfect pictures of themselves and their children. Mr. Cummins produces all kinds of work, from the carte de visite to the imperial cabinet. He makes a speciality of life-size portraits in crayon, oil, pastel, and India ink, and his water-color miniatures are the finest that can be executed. One of the most recent improvements in this art is the introduction of gelatine plates, by which photographs are now taken in less than a second, thus securing an ease of pose and natural expression hitherto almost unattainable. Mr. Cummins also deals extensively in photographic requisites and supplies of every description, and publishes a catalogue which for completeness and excellence of arrangement is unsurpassed by those of the most noted houses in Philadelphia, New York, or Boston. Having thus briefly sketched the facilities of this responsible house. it only remains to be added that its business has been conducted on the enduring principles of equity, and relations once entered into with it are certain to become pleasant and permanent. HCP.

****

D'ALMAINE, GEORGE, photographer, portrait painter.
Born in England, 1822; advertised that he had come to Baltimore to do portraits in pastel and crayon (1853); 91 W. Baltimore (1863-1864); 54 1/2 N. Charles (1865-1871); left Baltimore in 1884 probably for Peoria, Illinois where his wife's family owned property. U.S.C. 1870, CD, BD, PM.

DAMPF, J.H. & CO., photographer.
Over 105 W. Baltimore (1864-1866); Corning, New York (ca. 1880). CD, imprint on carte de visite, AC.

DARBY, ROBERT DOYNE, photographer.
321 N. Gay (1900-1901); 21 W. Lexington (1903); 106 W. Saratoga (1904). CD.

DASSAN, __________, photographer.
Photographer at the gallery of J.H. Whitehurst, 123 Baltimore (ca. 1863). Imprint on carte de visite, PC.

DAVIDAGE, LEWIS, ambrotypist.
Born in Maryland, 1817; $7000 value of personal property. U.S.C. 1860.

DAVIS, __________, photographer.
"I would call the attention of the public to those beautiful GEM PICTURES taken at DAVIS'S (sic) GALLERY, 68 EAST BALTIMORE STREET. Four for 35 cents, stamps included." TS, March 13, 1866.

DAVIS, J. WISTAR, daguerreotypist.
14 & 15 Franklin Buildings, corner North & Baltimore (1847-1849). CD.

DAVIS, WILLIAM, daguerreotypist.
117 Baltimore (September 1853-1855); over 93 W. Baltimore (1856-1857); over 121 W. Baltimore (1858-1860); 63 E. Baltimore (1864-1868). TS, CD.

DAY, GEORGE E., photographer.
"Old Town Studio," 321 N. Gay (1894-1895); 1119 Light (1896-1902); Day Brothers, 1119 Light and 926 N. Gay (1903). CD.

De La FRANC, FRANCIS, photographer.
300 N. Gay (1863); over 23 & 25 W. Baltimore (1867-1868). CD.

DELRUNE, B., photographer.
63 E. Baltimore (1859-1860). CD.

DePOITIERS, GUSTAVUS W., photographer.
1638 Miller (1897); 1328 McHenry (1898-1900); 303 S. Poppleton (1901); 949 N. Washington (1902-1903); 803 N. Bond (1904). CD.

DERR, SAMUEL M., photographer.
1101 Winchester (1902-1903);1126 N. Fremont Ave. (1903-1904). SD, BD.

DICKINSON, GEORGE W., photographer.
244 W. Baltimore (1856-1858). CD, TS.

DIEHL, MARTIN, photographer.
263 W. Baltimore (1867). CD.

DINMORE & LISTER, photographers.
20 N. Charles (1874). CD.

DINMORE & WILSON, photographers.
125 W. Baltimore (1872); N. Charles (1873). CD.

DINMORE, CHRISTOPHER, photographer.
213 W. Baltimore (1867-1868). CD.

DINMORE, WALTER, photographer.
213 W. Baltimore (1868-1870); Baltimore near South (1871). CD.

DOBSON, WILSON & BOWERMAN, photographers.
230 W. Lexington (1902). CD.

DONALDSON, GEORGE G., photographer.
21 W. Lexington (1902). CD.

DORSEY, CHARLES F., photographer.
Listed as a charter member of the National Photographic Association. PP, July 1869.

DUKEHART, FEDER, photographer.
357 W. Baltimore (1871-1872); 354 W. Baltimore (1873); 357 W. Baltimore (1874-1875). CD.

DUKEHART, FEDERICK, photographer.
877 W. Franklin (1897-1899). CD.

DUKEHART, HENRY F., photographer.
Born in Saxony, 1849; living in the 14th Ward. U.S.C. 1880.

DURANT, W.L., photographer.
55 Lexington (1882). CD.

DUVALL,__________, photographers.
and Co., over 65 W. Baltimore (1876); and Harvey, (1877-1878). Imprint on tintype, AC, CD.

DYER, WALTER J.L., photographer.
Born in Maryland, 1843; 468 W. Baltimore (1872); 144 Pennsylvania Ave. (1873-1864). U.S.C. 1870, CD.

****

ECONOMICAL HALF-TONE SUPPLY, dealers of photographic supplies.
9 E. Lexington (1899); 12 E. Lexington (1900-1901). CD.

EDKINS, JOSEPH, photographer.
103 Baltimore (1864); over 159 W. Baltimore (1867-1868). Imprint on carte de visite, AC, CD.

EDMONDSON, JOHN J., photographer.
Born in Maryland, 1833; living in the 10th Ward. U.S.C. 1880.

EDWARDS, FREDERICK W., photographer.
Born in Virginia, 1848; living in the 5th Ward. U.S.C. 1870.

EDWARDS, WILLIAM, photographer.
350 N. Gay (1878). CD.

ELLERBROCK, HERMAN H., photographer.
17 W. Lexington (1898); Broadway corner Mullikin (1899). CD.

ENKLE, J.S., photographer.
25 W. Baltimore (1863-1864). CD.

ENSEY, MARCELLUS P., daguerreotypist.
127 Broadway (November 1857-1859). TS, CD.

ERNSBERGER, JACOB, photographer.
21 Orleans (1886). CD.

ERNSBERGER, JOHN D., photographer.
1123 Orleans (1887); 419 W. Baltimore (1888); 501 N. Gay (1889); 588 N. Gay (1894-1898); solar copying, 11 N. Gay (1903). CD.

ERNSBERGER, JOSEPH D., photographer.
306 W. Lexington (1900). CD.

EVERITT, FRANCIS A., photographer.
Born in Maryland, 1845; living in the 16th Ward. U.S.C. 1870.

EXCELSIOR ART STUDIO (THE), photographers.
5 N. Charles (ca. 1900). Imprint on cabinet card, AC.

****

FAITHFUL, JOSEPH, daguerreotypist.
NE. corner Eutaw & Lexington (1851-1860). CD.

FENGE, HENRY, photographer.
Born in Baltimore, Oct. 10, 1851; partner with J.P. Blessing in Blessing & Co. studio. BD. (See Blessing & Co.)

Portrait of Henry Fitz, Jr. who opened the first daguerrean portrait studio in Maryland. History of Photography Collection, Smithsonian Institution

FIELD, SOLOMON, photographer.
Born in Hesse Darmstadt, 1825; living in the 7th Ward.
U.S.C. 1870.

FIELDS, HARRY, photographer.
Born in Maryland, 1856; living in the 5th Ward. U.S.C. 1880.

FISCHER & BRO., photographers.
103 W. Baltimore (1859-1864); 95 Baltimore (1864-1865). CD, imprint on CDV, AC.

FISHER, ARTHUR F., photographer.
Born in Maryland, 1837; 103 W. Baltimore (1858). $1500 value of personal property. CD, U.S.C. 1860.

FITZ, HENRY, JR., daguerreotypist, telescope maker.
112 Baltimore (summer 1840-November 1840); corner Baltimore & Harrison (November 1840-July 1841); 112 Baltimore (July 1841-fall 1842). TS, CD.

FITZGERALD, JAMES, photographer.
28 N. Charles (1883-1886); 206 N. Charles (1887). CD.

FLATTRE, ISAAC, photographer.
254 S. Bond (1896). CD.

FLICKENSCHILDT, HENRY N., photographer.
515 S. Broadway (1889-1892); 1710 Eastern Avenue (1894-1895); 515 S. Broadway (1896-1900). CD.

FLINT, __________, DR., daguerreotypist.
Advertisement for "Photographic Miniatures, Hall over the Watchmen Engine House, Light St." TS, September 14, 1848.

FLOYD & HARRYMAN, photographers.
5 W. Lexington (1903). CD.

FONTAYNE (CHARLES H.) & PORTER (WILLIAM S.), daguerreotypists.
268 Baltimore (1844-1845); Fontayne moves to Cincinnati, Ohio (1846); joined there by Porter (1848). TS, AD.
(see William S. Porter)

FORWOOD, JOHN S., photographer.
1706 Point Lane (1896). CD.

FOWX, EGBERT G., photographer.
Born in Kentucky, 1821; 1 N. Gay (1868-1875); 51 N. Eutaw (1877-1879); 264 E. Fayette (1880-1881); received Pat. No. 95,892 on October 19, 1869 for photographic printing method.
U.S.C. 1870, CD, PR.

FRANCE, RINGGOLD, photographer.
Corner Eutaw & Clay (1872-1875). CD.

FREEBURGER, ALEX C., photographer.
249 Light (1875); 255 Light (1877-1881); 709 Light (1887-1889); 17 E. Baltimore (1899-1901); 644 Baltimore (1902). CD.

FREEBURGER, MARGARET E., photographer.
713 Light (1894-1899). CD.

FRENCH, GLORIA, photographer.
Gloria French Photo Studio, 246 S. Broadway (ca. 1895). Imprint on a photographic portrait, PC.

FRENCH PHOTOGRAPHIC ACADEMY OF ART, photographers.
155 W. Baltimore (ca. 1880). Imprint on carte de visite, AC.

FULDS, S., photographer.
163 N. Gay (1863-1864); Broadway (1871) CD, BD.

FUHRMAN, WILLIAM H., photographer.
303 or 313 Falls Road (1894); 303 Falls Road (1895); 242 Morling Avenue (1896-1898). CD.

****

GAMBRILL, WILLIAM B., photographer.
453 N. Fremont (1877-1878). CD.

GANTT, MARTIN, daguerreotypist.
Born in Maryland, 1838; living in the 19th Ward. U.S.C. 1860.

GARRETT, H.W., photographer.
123 W. Baltimore (1875); 1063 W. Baltimore (1879); 114 Lexington (1880). CD.

GASSAWAY, JULIA, photograph painter.
Born in Cuba, 1841; living in the 9th Ward. U.S.C. 1870.

GARTHWAIT, ISAAC, daguerreotypist.
Over 97 1/2 Baltimore (1842). CD.

GEBREGE, ANTON, daguerreotypist.
Born in Prussia, 1842; living in the 1st Ward. U.S.C. 1860.

GERMAN, JOSEPH, photographer.
Over 234 Lexington (1865-1867). CD, imprint on CDV, AC.

GETZ, WILLIAM, photographer.
Over 103 W. Baltimore (1878); over 42 N. Charles (1879-1886); 210 N. Charles (1887-1889); 212 N. Charles (1894); 210 N. Charles (1895-1897); 212 N. Charles (1898); 210 N. Charles (1899-1904). CD.

GIDDINGS, S.B., photographer.
Mentioned as an employee at the gallery of Richard Walzl; "This gentleman has been fortunate in securing the services of Mr. S.B. GIDDINGS, whose Photographs were so universally admired at the last exhibition of the Maryland Institute. Mr. Giddings has already won for himself a reputation unsurpassed for the accuracy with which he portrays the features, gracefulness of position, and fascinating style of Pictures." TS, October 29, 1866.
(see Richard Walzl)

GLEDHILL, GEORGE, daguerreotypist.
217 Baltimore (February 1854-1857). TS, CD.

GOLDENSKY, ABRAHAM B., photographer.
633 W. Fayette (1902). CD.

GORHAM & TUCKER, daguerreotypists.
Joined seven other daguerreotypists in petitioning the Baltimore City Council for permission to erect sidewalk displays of "Daguerreotype Specimens" (March 7, 1850). RG 16, H.R.S. 1850, Document 318, Baltimore City Archives.

GRANT, A.G., ambrotypist, photographer.
Mentioned in an advertisement for the gallery of P.L. Perkins that he would instruct in the "art of photography, Ambrotyping and every process connected with the business." TS, December 6, 1855. (see Palmer L. Perkins)

GREEN, JAMES, Philosophical Instrument Maker and Daguerreotype Experimenter.
Made the first daguerreotypes in Baltimore with the assistance of Thomas Phillips. BA, October 31, 1839.

GREEN, JOHN, daguerreotypist.
Corner Baltimore & Charles (1849-1851); 148 E. Madison (1858-1859). CD.

GREEN, JOHN, JR., daguerreotypist.
Living at 216 S. Charles (1853-1854). CD.

GRESHOFF, HENRY, photographer.
69 Pearl (1881-1885). CD.

GRILL, GOTTFRIED, photographer.
113 N. Washington (1883-1884). CD.

GRINAGE, WILLIAM H.B., photographer.
590 W. Biddie (1894-1896); 1136 Pennsylvania Ave. (1901-1902). SD, CD.

GROENINGER, WILLIAM J., photographer.
404 N. Paca (1899); 1200 Battery Ave. (1900); 404 N. Paca (1901-1904). CD.

GROMINGER, WILLIAM, photographer.
Born in Maryland, 1857; living in the 12th Ward. U.S.C. 1880.

GUMBINSKI, LEON, photographer.
105 N. Gay (1877-1878); 107 N. Gay (1880). CD.

****

HAGADORN, FRANK T., stereoview publisher.
160 Saratoga (1870); Howard House (1871-1872); 5 S. Calvert St (1873-1882); and Bixby (1883); and Shenbrooks, Calverton (1884); publisher of the "Gems of American Scenery- Baltimore & Ohio Railroad and its branches" series. CD, AC.

HALL, HENRY S., photographer.
Born in England, 1840. U.S.C. 1860.

HALLWIG, O., photographer.
Born in Saxony, 1840; and Co. 20 N. Charles (1868-1870); and Busey (1870-1871). U.S.C. 1870, CD, imprint on carte de viste, AC, PF. (see Norval H. Busey)

HALWIG, AUGUSTUS, photographer.
Born in Germany, 1812; living in the 15th Ward. U.S.C. 1880.

HALWIG, PRONO, artist and photographer.
Born in Germany, 1842; living in the 15th Ward; son of Augustus Halwig. U.S.C. 1880.

HAMBURGER, BEN (ART CO.), photographers.
326 N. Charles and 327 N. Gay (1902). CD.

HAMILTON, T., photographer.
Born in Maryland, 1843. U.S.C. 1860.

HAMMOND, JOHN, photographer, photo-copying.
Over 16 N. Charles (1886). CD.

HAMPE, FRANCIS W., photographer.
Born in Maryland, 1845; 147 Lexington (1868-1870); 163 N. Gay (1871); 154 Harford Ave. (1872). CD.

HAPE, SAMUEL, daguerreotypist, photographer.
and Kuhn, 207 1/2 W. Baltimore (1856-1857); Hape only (1858); with Perkins & Co., 196 N. Eutaw (1858-1859). CD.

HARDING, EDWARD S., photographer.
Born in Maryland, 1841; 194 Lexington (1877); 180 Lexington (1878); 22 N. Eutaw (1879-1883). U.S.C. 1880, CD.

HARKNEY, JOHN J., photographer.
Born in Scotland, 1844; living in the 4th Ward. U.S.C. 1880.

HARRIMAN, KENDALL F., photographer.
5 N. Charles (1895-1896). CD.

HARRIS, WILLIAM S.J., photographer.
2618 Mary (1894-1895); 1711 N. Calhoun (1899). CD.

HATTON, ISAIAH W., photographer.
504 Druid Hill Ave. (1902). CD.

HAWKES, BENJAMIN F., photographer.
Former operator at Whitehurst's Daguerrean Gallery, Richmond (1856?); 205 Baltimore (Oct. 1857-1859); took over the old Whitehurst Gallery after being employed there as an operator. PV, CD, BD.

HEBBEL, JULIUS, photographer.
19 E. Baltimore (1873-1874); 409 N. Gay (1889-1904); 327 N. Gay (1895-1904); 321 N. Gay (1903). CD.

HELLMAN, J.B., photographer.
Operator at the gallery of George Wunder, 333 W. Baltimore (ca. 1867). Imprint on tintype, AC.

HELMICH, J. GUSTAVE, photographer, photographic retoucher.
272 S. Broadway (1880); 472 W. Baltimore (1882); mentioned as a former retoucher for J.S. Cummins before opening his own business in 1882. CD, IM. (see J.S. Cummins)

HENKEL & CO., photographers.
644 W. Baltimore (1894). CD.

HENNING, CHARLES, photographer.
157 S. Broadway (1879). CD.

HESS, JOHN P., photographer.
SW. corner Baltimore & Poppleton (1874). CD.

HESSE, WILLIAM, daguerreotypist.
104 N. Eutaw (1855-1856); 72 Raborg (1856-1857). CD.

HEWETT, HENRY C., photographer.
Born in Maryland, 1845; living in the 9th Ward; brother-in-law of Egbert G. Fowx; 103 S. Exeter (1867-1868). U.S.C. 1870, CD.

HEWITT, GEORGE W., photographer.
9 N. Gay (1867-1875); Hewitt & Bowerman, 1 N. Gay (1877-1879). Imprint on tintypes, CD.

HINKLE, ADAM, daguerreotypist, photographer.
531 W. Baltimore (1856-1860); over 327 W. Baltimore (1864-1866). CD, BD.

HITCHENS, JOHN H., stereoview dealer.
"Toys & Fancy Goods," 71 W. Baltimore (1880-1882). Imprint on stereoviews, AC.

HOHLWEG, JOHN, photographer.
Over 531 and 427 W. Baltimore (1871). BD.

HOHLWEG, LOUIS, photographer.
Born in Prussia, 1847; 531 W. Baltimore (1865-1883). CD, HCP.

HOHLWEG (HOLWIG), VALENTINE, daguerreotypist, photographer.
Born Coa Hassan, 1840; 427 Baltimore (1870). U.S.C. 1860, CD.

HOHLWEG (HOLWIG), VINCENT, daguerreotypist, photographer.
Born Coa Hassan, 1803; $1000 value of personal property; 531 W. Baltimore between Pine & Fremont (1863-1880). U.S.C. 1860, CD.

HOHLWEG (HOLWIG), WILLIAM, daguerreotypist.
Born Coa Hassan, 1836; living in 20th Ward. U.S.C. 1860.

HOLYLAND, HARRIET, photographer.
Born in England, 1808; living in the 6th Ward. U.S.C. 1870.

HOLYLAND, JOHN, photographer.
Born in New Jersey, 1842; "Late Young's Gallery," 231 W. Baltimore (1865-1880); 229 W. Baltimore (1881-1886); 3 W. Baltimore after renumbering (1887-1889); 7 W. Lexington (1899-1902). U.S.C. 1880, CD.

> J. Holyland, Gallery of Artistic Photography, Southwest corner of Baltimore and Charles Streets.- Mr. J. Holyland conducts one of the leading photographic establishments in the city. The gallery is commodious in dimensions and finely furnished, due regard being had for the comfort of visitors, and the operating rooms are supplied with the most modern appliances and devices calculated to facilitate and improve production. Mr. Holyland gives his experienced attention to every branch of the photographic art, and

his work is distinguished for the admirable effects obtained. Brilliancy and the highest degree of permanency are the results sought after, together with pleasing resemblance and satisfaction to both proprietor and customers. The gallery enjoys a wide popularity and has been favorably known to the public for over twenty years. The business was originally started in Washington City in 1861, was transferred to Baltimore in 1865, and its career has been one of great prosperity. HCP.

HOOD & CO., daguerreotypists.
123 Baltimore (1850). TS.

HOOPER, WILLIAM H., photographer.
Born in Maryland, 1856; living in the 1st Ward. U.S.C. 1880.

HORWELL, EDWARD C., daguerreotypist.
SE. corner Gay & Front (1847-1850); Baltimore, dwelling 128 N. Exeter (1851); 207 1/2 Baltimore, dwelling 127 N. Exeter (1855-1856). TS, CD.

HORWELL, ELLSWORTH M., daguerreotypist.
In partnership with Edward A. Pindell, 103 W. Baltimore (1856-1857). CD.

HUGHES, ANDREW W., daguerreotypist.
Agent for Plumbe's National Daguerrean Gallery, 265 Baltimore (1849-1850); residence at 112 Aisquith (1855-1857). CD.

HUGHES, JAMES, photographer.
Born in Maryland, 1857; 84 Patterson Ave. (1881-1882); 125 St. Paul (1883). U.S.C. 1880, CD.

HUGHES, JAMES F. CO. (THE), commercial photography.
1106 Riggs Ave. (1881-1882); 17-19 E. Baltimore (1904). CD.

HULL & GOTT, photographers.
109 Lexington (1877). CD.

HUNTER, PLEASANT C., photographer.
109 Lexington (1879); Culpeper, Va. (ca. 1880); Martinsburg, W. Va. (ca. 1885). CD, imprint on CDV, PC, imprint on cabinet card, AC.

HUTH, HUGO, photographer.
1306 Andre (1902-1904). SD, CD.

****

IDE, LOUIS, photographer.
"Successor to Louis Walzl," 65 W. Baltimore (1865-1866). CD.

ILGENFRITZ, JOSEPH L., photographer.
5 W. Lexington (1896-1899); 20 W. Lexington (1900-1904). CD.

IMPERIAL STUDIO, photographers,
21 E. Baltimore (1892-1895); Eutaw corner of Franklin (1896-1899). CD.

IRVING & RIGBY, photographers.
65 W. Baltimore (1879). CD.

ISRAEL, ELIZABETH, photographer.
Born in the West Indies, 1790. U.S.C. 1860.

ISRAEL, STEPHEN, photographer.
Born in New York, 1826; over 91 W. Baltimore (1858-1860); and Co., over 125 W. Baltimore (April 1860-1868). U.S.C. 1860, CD.

****

JACKSON, JAMES A., photographer.
Listed as a charter member of the National Photographic Association. PP, July 1869.

JACKSON, ROBERT F., photographer.
110 Hanover (1882); 46 S. Eutaw (1883). CD.

JARDEN, S., photographist.
Advertised as taking "Plumb's Patent Colored Photographs" at the Baltimore Museum. TS, May 29, 1843.

JARDEN, SAMUEL, daguerreotypist.
SE. corner of Gough and Broadway (1853-1854). CD.

JEFFRES, EDWARD W., photographer.
508 S. Broadway (1894-1895). CD.

JEFFRES, HARRY J., photographer.
106 N. Charles (1900-1904). CD.

JEFFRES & ROGERS, photographers.
112 N. Charles (1894-1899). CD.

JEFFRIES, JAMES, photographer.
Born in Virginia, 1835; living in the 16th Ward. U.S.C. 1870.

JENKINS, J.J., photographer.
99 Baltimore (ca. 1862). Imprint on carte de visite, AC.

JENKINS, WILLIAM K., photographer.
125 W. Baltimore (1870). CD.

JOHNSON, JOHN W., works in photography gallery.
Black, born in Maryland, 1825; living in the 11th Ward.
U.S.C. 1880.

JOHNSON, JOSEPH, photographer.
73 W. Baltimore (1863-1864). CD.

JOHNSON, THOMAS, photographer.
Born in Maryland, 1842; living in the 6th Ward. U.S.C. 1880.

JOHNSON, W.R., photographic stock & supplies.
38 S. Charles (1865-1867). CD.

JOHNSTON, JOHN R., portraitist, photographic colorist.
Colorist of the Whitehurst photographic entry in the 1856 Maryland Institute Exhibition; "Col. John R. Johnston has painted many oil pictures of J.H. Whitehurst's. He is now painting for three or four of the galleries, and with the many orders he has for himself and the different galleries, he is kept busy nearly all the time. Col. J. has his studio in Carroll Hall corner Calvert and Baltimore Streets, where a visit to him sometimes will pay all who go to see his many portraits."
TS, October 25, 1856. PFAJ.

JONES, HENRY & CO., stereoview dealer.
"Crescent Dollar Store," 220 W. Baltimore (1874-1879). CD.

JONES, JOHN, daguerreotypist.
Jones' Daguerrian Gallery, 159 Baltimore (1848-1851). TS, CD.

JONES, JOHN H., photographer.
609 N. Eutaw (1903-1904). CD.

JONES, R.T. & CO., photographers.
101 N. Gay (1874-1875). CD.

JONES, ROBERT, photographer.
Born in Maryland, 1855; living in the 14th Ward. U.S.C. 1880.

****

KAMPMANN, AUTHUR, photographer.
Corner of Light & Baltimore (1856-1857). CD.

KAYLOR, THOMAS, daguerreotypist.
150 S. Paca (1856-1857). CD.

KENNEDY, THOMAS F., photographer.
Born in Maryland, 1840; 48 N. Charles (1873). CD.

KERLINGER, LEWIS H., photographer.
154 Myrtle Avenue (1875); 28 1/2 Argyle Avenue (1877-1878). CD.

KING, B.F., daguerreotypist.
217 Baltimore (1846-August 1850). TS, CD.

KING, MRS. B.F., daguerreotypist.
217 Baltimore (1849-1850). CD.

KING, F.W. & RICHARD, daguerreotype suppliers and manufacturers.
33 South Street (1853-May 1854); 226 Baltimore (May 1854-1859). CD, TS, May 25, 1854.

KING, WILLIAM, photographer.
48 N. Charles (1884). CD.

KING, WILLIAM & BRO., photographer's stock.
2 N. Liberty (1863-1872). CD.

KINLING, WILLIAM, photographer.
508 S. Broadway (1899-1901); 302 S. Eden (1902); 508 S. Broadway (1903-1904). CD.

KIRKNESS, JOHN J., photographer.
2 W. Baltimore (1886); 718 E. Baltimore (1887); 613 E. Baltimore (1894-1896); 1517 Federal (1897-1898); 720 Pennsylvania (1899); 604 N. Eutaw (1900-1901); 230 N. Fremont Avenue (1902-1904). CD.

KIRKNESS, JOHN J. JR., photographer.
401 S. Broadway (1900-1902). CD, BD.

KLINGELHOFER, FREDERICK F., photographer.
and Bowie, 58 Lexington (1868-1870); Klingelhofer only (1870-1871). CD, BD.

KLOTZSCH, FREDERICK J., photographer.
425 E. Baltimore (1899); 1411 E. Pratt (1900); 428 E. Baltimore (1901); 1411 E. Pratt (1902); 1632 E. Chase (1903). CD.

KNOWLTON, WILLIAM S., photographer.
72/73 W. Baltimore (1870-1873). CD.

KOESTENER, WILLIAM H., photographer.
Born in Bavaria, 1859; over 9 1/2 W. Baltimore (1881-1882); 102 N. Caroline (1883-1895); 102 N. Charles (1893-1897); 100 N. Charles (1896); 13 S. Broadway (1898). U.S.C. 1880, CD.

KORN, CHARLES, photographer.
472 W. Baltimore (1863-1864). CD.

KRAUS, ELLA, photographer.
1316 Pennsylvania Avenue (1902). CD.

KRAUTES, WILLIAM, apprentice to photographer.
Born in Maryland, 1852; living in the 17th Ward. U.S.C. 1870.

KUHN, FRANK, daguerreotypist.
Hape & Kuhn, over 207 1/2 W. Baltimore (1856-1857). CD.

KUHN, FRANK, photographer.
"Late E. Balch," 48 N. Charles (1873-1880); and 50 N. Charles (1879-1880); Kuhn & Cummins (1874-1880). CD.

****

LALLEY, L.H., photographer.
Born in Maryland, 1856; living in the 9th Ward. U.S.C. 1880.

LAMB, F.F., daguerreotypist.
Mentioned as proprietor of "J.D. Marsters' well known rooms at 147 Lexington Street" TS, November 22, 1859. (see J.D. Marsters)

LANGDON, ________, ambrotypist.
159 Baltimore (1855); the first photographer to offer "ambrotypes or imperishable pictures on glass" in Baltimore.
TS, May 15, 1855.

LANGLEY, JOSEPH P., photographer.
822 S. Canton (1900-1903); 1323 N. Broadway (1904). CD.

LANSDALE, ROBERT VINTON, daguerreotypist, ambrotypist, photographer.
Over 293 W. Baltimore (1858-1860); supposedly took the first daguerreotype of Madame Jermoe Bonaparte, wife of Napoleon's brother Jerome, who was the former Betsy Paterson of Baltimore; took David Bachrach, Jr., who later established his own successful gallery, as his apprentice in 1860; Bachrach described Lansdale in his memoirs as "different from most of the leading artists, more intelligent and full of the experimental spirit" and "a man of high moral character and free from the scandals connected with some of the leading photographers." CD, PA.

LAUSCH, HENRY F., photographer.
Born in Hanover, 1845; living in the 15th Ward. U.S.C. 1880.

LEACH, CHARLES, photographer.
Leach & Edkins, 93 W. Baltimore (1864); 159 W. Baltimore (1868-1871); Charles Leach only, 159 W. Baltimore (1872-1873); over 217 W. Baltimore (1874-1877); 211 W. Baltimore (1878-1881); 207 W. Baltimore (1882-1886); 17 E. Baltimore (1887); 19 E. Baltimore (1888-1889); 17 E. Baltimore (1894); 19 E. Baltimore (1895). CD.

LEACH, WILLIAM, ambrotypist, photographer.
Coss, Leach & Irwin, 127 Baltimore (1860); Leach & Damp, 127 W. Baltimore (1863-1864); Leach only, 127 W. Baltimore (ca. 1865); 159 Baltimore (ca. 1866); over 127 W. Baltimore (1868-1870). CD, imprints on cartes de visite, AC.

LEE, ELISHA, photographic canvas preparer.
"Mr. Elisha Lee has gone into the business of preparing canvas for photographic prints very largely; his canvas is superior to any other I have ever seen tried, and he deserves to be patronized for his untiring labors in perfecting this composition, whereby the photograph can be printed on and painted equal to paper." PFAJ, September 1857.

LEE, ELIJAH, photographist.
99 1/2 Baltimore (1858-1859). CD.

LEE, GEORGE A., photographer.
265 W. Pratt (1858-1859). CD.

LEVY, LEWIS E., photographer.
268 W. Baltimore (1875). CD.

LEVYTYPE PHOTO-ENGRAVING CO.
103 W. Fayette (1877). CD.

LINGEMAN, HENRY, photographer.
Born in Maryland, 1853; living in the 17th Ward. U.S.C. 1870.

LISTER & CO., photographers.
20 N. Charles (1875). CD.

LISTER, NELSON, photographer's apprentice.
Born in Maryland, 1858; living in the 19th Ward. U.S.C. 1870.

LOANE, E.D. JR. CO. (THE), dealers of photographic supplies.
14 W. Lexington (1898). CD.

LOGAN, J.L. & CO., daguerreotypists.
SW. corner of Baltimore & South (1853-1854). CD.

LONDON STUDIO, photographers.
5 W. Lexington (1894-1895). CD.

LORENTZ & RITTER, photographers.
Corner Leadenhall, Stockholm & West (1873). CD.

LOWRY, JOSEPH T., photographers.
493 W. Fayette (1875); 526 W. Fayette (1877); 20 N. Gilmor (1878-1881); 131 E. Baltimore (1892-1904). CD, SD.

LUMPKIN, E.S., photographer.
66 Lexington (1883). CD.

LUPUS, EDWARD, photographer.
23 Baltimore (ca. 1863); over SW. corner Baltimore & Centre market space (1864). Imprint on a carte de viste, PC, CD.

LURM, EDWARD, electic photographer.
Born in Maryland, 1851; living in the 18th Ward. U.S.C. 1880.

LUSBY, CHARLES P., photographer.
Born in Maryland, 1843; Lusby & Leach, over 127 W. Baltimore (1871); Charles Lusby, over 127 W. Baltimore (1872-1875); 91 W. Baltimore (1877-1886); 403 E. Baltimore (1887-1888); 425 E. Baltimore (1889). CD.

LUSBY, ROBERT, photographer.
Born in Maryland, 1837; living in the 9th Ward. U.S.C. 1880.

****

McALLISTER, F.W. & CO., dealers of photographic stock.
3 N. Charles (1898-1904). CD.

McCABE, PROFESSOR ____________, photographer.
704 W. Lexington (1897). Imprint on a photograph, AC.

McCABE, HUGH J. & CO., photographers,
510 W. Baltimore (1900); 875 W. Lombard (1901); 1039 W. Lexington (1902-1903). CD, SD.

McCARRIER & HUNTER, photographers,
58 N. Charles (1873). CD.

McCARRIER, JAMES, photographer.
Born in Maryland, 1837; 9 & 11 W. Baltimore (1862-1864); 149 E. Monument (1874); 147 E. Monument (1875); 163 N. Gay (1877). Trade cards, AC, CD.

McCLEARY, ULYSSES G., photographer.
1733 Friendsbury Place (1896). CD.

McGREGOR, ___________, photographic colorist.
Mentioned as the "celebrated Photographic Colorist" employed at the gallery of Palmer L. Perkins, 99 Baltimore.
TS, September 19, 1856.

McKIGGAN, MRS. A.E., photographer.
Over 20 N. Charles (1877). CD.

McMURRAY, R.R. & CO., photographers.
2 & 4 N. Greene (1867-1868). CD.

McPHERSON, ROBERT A., daguerreotypist, ambrotypist.
234 Lexington (1851, 1858-1859). CD.

MARKS, H.J., daguerreotypist.
500 plates on hand; 2 male employees; $80 average monthly labor cost; 2500 likenesses produced yearly. U.S.M.C. 1850.

MARKS, HENRY R., daguerreotypist.
117 Baltimore (1848-May 1851); partner with Jacob Shew (1848-April 1850); 159 Baltimore (November 1851-1853); removed to 57 Dauphin Street, Mobile Alabama (1855-1858); Austin, Texas (1875); $1500 capital invested, 500 plates on hand, 3 male employees, $140 average monthly labor cost, 5000 likenesses produced yearly. CD, TS, AD, PP, U.S.M.C. 1850. (see Jacob Shew)

MARSHALL, FRANK, apprentice to photographer.
Born in Portugal, 1863; living in the 17th Ward. U.S.C. 1880.

MARSTERS, JOSEPH D., daguerreotypist.
147 Lexington (1850-1860). TS, CD.

MARTIN, CHARLES, photographer.
511 E. Baltimore (1894-1896); 321 N. Gay (1897). CD.

MARYLAND PHOTO AND CRAYON CO., photographers.
644 W. Baltimore (1892). CD.

MARYLAND PHOTOGRAPHIC COPYING CO., MURRIL & WOODWARD, proprietors.
561 Saratoga (1879-1880). CD.

MASON, H.M. & CO., photographers.
1519 E. Pratt (1888); and Brother, 153 1/2 E. Pratt (1889). CD.

MASSICOTT, WILLIAM, photographer.
234 W. Lexington (1863-1864). CD.

MAYFIELD & DARBY, photographers.
822 E. Baltimore (1899). CD.

MENTZEL, CHARLES, photographer.
515 N. Stricker (1900); Mentzel & Derr, 1126 N. Fremont (1901). CD.

MERRITT, J.D. & CO., photographers.
Over 66 Lexington (1882). CD.

MESNY, J. DE GIFFARD, photographer.
226 N. Charles (1898-1904). CD.

METZUNG, FRANK J., photographer.
42 N. Eutaw (1874); 472 W. Baltimore (1883-1886); 207 N. Gilmor (1887); 229 N. Gay (1896); 327 N. Gay (1898). CD.

MEWBURN, JOSEPH, photographer.
73 W. Baltimore (1867-1868); 603 W. Lombard (1878). CD.

MILDE, JOHN W.F., daguerreotypist.
45 Hampstead (1855-1856). CD.

MILES & WINDSOR, photographers.
Over 205 W. Baltimore (1864-1866). CD.

MILLER, HARRY R., photographer's apprentice.
Born in Maryland, 1854; living in the 19th Ward. U.S.C. 1870.

MILLER, WILLIAM J., ambrotypist, photographer.
256 W. Pratt (1858-1868). CD.

MILNER, G.C., photographer.
Born in England, 1855; living in the 4th Ward. U.S.C. 1880.

MINIFIE, WILLIAM & SON, dealers of photographic supplies.
5 N. Charles (1879-1885); 7 N. Charles (1886). CD.

MOLTZ, HENRY, photographer.
Born in Switzerland, 1835; 217 W. Baltimore (1863-1871); Moltz & Philips (1871). CD.

MOMENTHY, EMAIL, photographer.
536 W. Baltimore (1871); 531 W. Baltimore (1872-1873). CD.

MONTAGUE, HENRY, photographer.
Born in Virginia, 1820; living in the 15th Ward. U.S.C. 1870.

MONUMENTAL PHOTOGRAPH CO., photographic sellers.
118 W. Baltimore (ca. 1866). Imprint on carte de visite, PC.

MONUMENTAL PHOTOGRAPHIC CO., photographers.
120 Lexington (1885-1886); 203 W. Lexington (1887). CD.

MOORE, CHARLES H., photographer.
330 N. Charles (1899). CD.

MOORE, WILLIAM B., photographer.
321 N. Gay (1899). CD.

MORAWETZ, L.F., inventor.
Received patent no. 59,438 on November 6, 1866 for a vertical solar camera. PR.

MORRIS, JOHN H., daguerreotypist.
33 S. Gay (1856-1857); 105 W. Baltimore (1859). CD, BD.

MORROW, J.H., photographer, inventor.
105 W. Baltimore (1858-1860); received patent no. 17,066 on April 14, 1857 for a photographic bath process. CD, PR.

MOSHER, CALVIN S., photographer.
Born in Nova Scotia, 1826; 465 W. Baltimore (1875-1881); 719 W. Baltimore (1882-1883). U.S.C. 1880, CD.

MOTT, C.F., photographer.
Born in Bavaria, 1855; living in the 9th Ward. U.S.C. 1880.

MOULTON, ___________, daguerreotypist.
81 Baltimore (1848); "Mr. Moulton has taken rooms on the first floor...where he is prepared to take likenesses in the most perfect style, by the use of the Galvanic Battery, which insures a perfect eye and natural color, used altogether by the celebrated operators of Philadelphia to great success."
TS, April 16, 1848.

MUELLER, ANDREW, photographer.
515 S. Broadway (1903). CD.

MUELLER, GEORGE C., photographer, dealer of photographic supplies.
Born in Bavaria, 1851; Mueller & Bro., 247 Canton Avenue (1873-1874); 160 S. Broadway (1875-1886); George C. Mueller only (1880-1883); and Co. (1884-1889); 515 S. Broadway (1887-1888); 401 S. Broadway (1889-1899); 401 S. Broadway & 644 W. Baltimore (1894-1895); 5 W. Lexington (1902); Photographic Supplies, 306 W. Lexington (1899-1900). U.S.C. 1880, CD, SD.

MUELLER, HERMAN, photographer.
Over 9 W. Baltimore (1883). CD.

MUELLER, JOHN G., photographer.
247 Canton Ave. (1871). BD.

MULLAN, JOHN P., daguerreotypist.
SE. corner Baltimore & South (December 1849-1850). TS, CD.

MULLEN, E.M., photographer.
51 N. Eutaw (1879); 78 Pearl (1880-1881). CD.

MUNDER, T., photographer.
131 W. Baltimore (1863-1864). CD.

MURPHY, A. ALLEN & CO., photographers.
861 N. Howard (1901). CD.

MURPHY, D.H., dealer of photographers' stock.
Kellinger & Murphy, 109 Lexington (1879-1881); Murphy only (1880-1881). CD.

MURRAY, GEORGE W., photographer.
Born in Virginia, 1845; living in the 6th Ward. U.S.C. 1880.

MYERS & HEDIAN, photographers, dealers of photographic stock.
125 W. Baltimore (1868-1869); "Photographers' Stock", 33 W. Baltimore (1867). CD, BD.

MYERS, MOSES, photographer.
176 E. Baltimore (1877). CD.

****

NAIRN, J.C., daguerreotypist.
1 N. Calvert (1849); "Possessing a practical as well as scientific knowledge of the art acquired in part under Daguerre, and improved by experimental practice, good instruments and one of the best lights in Baltimore." TS, January 6, 1849.

NASH, MOLLY, photographer operator.
Born in Connecticut, 1829; living in the 6th Ward. U.S.C. 1870.

NATIONAL DAGUERREAN GALLERY, daguerreotypists.
126 Baltimore. TS, February 17, 1855.

NEWBURN, JOSEPH, photographer.
Born in Maryland, 1836; living in the 20th Ward. U.S.C. 1870.

NEW YORK PHOTO CO., photographers.
425 E. Baltimore (ca. 1885). Imprint on cabinet card, AC.

NEW YORK PHOTO JEWELRY CO.
218 E. Baltimore (1901); 1103 E. Baltimore (1902). CD.

NIMMO, CHARLES M., photographer.
123 W. Baltimore (1877); 62 Barry (1878). CD.

NIMMO, THOMAS J. & CO., daguerreotypists.
159 Baltimore (1854-1856); Frostburg, Md. (1875); former operator for J.H. Whitehurst. TS, CD, PP. (see Maryland Counties)

****

OBERDALLHOFF, W.H.E., photographer.
125 W. Baltimore (1883-1885). CD.

O'NEILL, HUGH, operator for J.H. Whitehurst.
Was asked to work in the gallery of Henry Pollock, who was not "able to fulfill engagements for want of help." However, "Mr. O'NEILL did not conclude to take the engagement" and continued in the employment of J.H. Whitehurst at his Washington gallery. PFAJ, 1857.

OPENHEIMER, MICHAEL, apprentice to photographer.
Born in Maryland, 1855; living in the 5th Ward. U.S.C. 1870.

ORIOLE PHOTO GALLERY, photographers.
327 N. Gay (1902-1903). SD.

ORIOLE PORTRAIT & VIEWING CO. (THE), photographers.
1316 Pennsylvania Ave. (1896). CD.

OSBORN & CO., photographers,
73 W. Baltimore (1859-1865). BD, stamp tax on CDV, AC.

****

PACK, WALTER, photographer.
307 N. Charles (1903); 5 W. Lexington (1904). CD.

PARIS STUDIO, photographers.
SW. corner Baltimore & Charles (ca. 1880). Imprint on cabinet card, AC.

PARKER & YOUNG, daguerreotypists.
97 Baltimore (November 27, 1841). TS.

PARLOW, GEORGE F.& CO., photographists.
103 Baltimore (1858). BD.

PASSANO, JOSEPH JR., photographer.
"Successor to Whitehurst & Co.," over 123 W. Baltimore (1867-1868). Imprint on carte de visite, AC, CD.

PAWER, M., photographer.
Born in Virginia, 1838. U.S.C. 1860.

PERKINS & CO., photographers.
217 W. Baltimore (1858-1860). CD.

PERKINS, HARRY L., photographer.
207 W. Baltimore (1872-1879); 103 W. Baltimore (1882-1886); 311 E. Baltimore (1887-1897); 21 E. Baltimore (1898-1904). CD.

> H. L. Perkins, Photographic Studio, No. 311 (old No. 103 West) East Baltimore Street, second door below the _Sun_ Office.-- One of the most prominent artists in this city is Mr. H. L. Perkins. This house was founded as far back as 1846, and is consequently one of the oldest in Baltimore. The house was founded by Mr. P. L. Perkins, and he retired from the business in 1880 in favor of his son, the present proprietor, Mr. H. L. Perkins, who has had a life's training in the business, and is regarded as an expert in it. The studio comprises two floors, each 25 x 80 feet in dimensions, and these are very handsomely furnished, and are fitted up with the most approved appliances and apparatus known to the profession, including splendid scenery, etc. A competent number of assistants is employed, and the finest work in all branches of photography is produced here. The clearness of amber and a lifelike expression mark the pictures, and it is this same transparent effect which has given them an excellent reputation, placing Mr. Perkins among the leading members of the photographic profession. Portraits are likewise made in oils, water colors, pastels, crayon, and in India ink in the highest style of the art. Mr. Perkins is a native of this city. HCP.

PERKINS, JOHN WESTON, daguerreotypist, photographer.
212 W. Baltimore (1856-1857); 211 W. Baltimore (1859-1868); 256 Pennsylvania (1883-1886); 1316 Pennsylvania (1887-1889, 1895-1901); 1218 Pennsylvania (1894); 680 W. Baltimore (1902). BD, CD.

> J. W. Perkins, Photograph Gallery, No. 256 Pennsylvania Avenue.- A prominent establishment in this city is that of Mr. J. W. Perkins, which was originally founded as a Daguerrean gallery thirty-eight years ago, at No. 211 Baltimore street, and from the date of its commencement has always maintained its supremacy in the profession. The premises occupied are spacious and commodious, comprising a very nicely furnished reception-room, while the operating and other departments are thoroughly equipped, and supplied with all the latest improved appliances known to the profession, including the dry-plate and the instantaneous processes. Mr. Perkins is prepared to execute all kinds of pictures, from the smallest locket to the life-size portrait, also to enlarge from small pictures to any size. Portraits are also executed in oil, water colors, pastel, crayon, and India ink in the highest style of art, at very low prices, and satisfaction guaranteed in all cases. His work cannot be excelled for truthful delineation, brilliancy of expression, and harmony of effect. Mr. Perkins is one of the oldest photographers in the State. He was born in Burlington county, N.J., and came to Baltimore in 1848. It can also be truthfully stated that he was one of the first individuals to take a photograph in the State. He is a member of the Masonic fraternity, I.O. of O.F., Knights of Pythias, Order of Chosen Friends, and Iron Hall. HCP.

PERKINS, PALMER LENFIELD, daguerreotypist, photographer.
Born New Jersey, 1824; Franklin Building, NE. corner North & Baltimore (1850-1857); and 211 Baltimore (1852-1856); and 99 W. Baltimore (1856-1857); 91 and 101 Baltimore (1858-1859); 99 and 207 W. Baltimore (1859-1864); and 101 W. Baltimore (1864); 205 and 207 W. Baltimore (1865-1870); 205 W. Baltimore (1870-1877); 207 W. Baltimore (1877-1879); 103 W. Baltimore (1880-1881); and Son (1881). U.S.C. 1860, BD, CD.

PERRY AND BRO., photographers.
121 W. Baltimore (1864). CD.

PERRY & COVER, photographers.
560 W. Baltimore (1867-1868). CD.

PHELPS, T.W.S., photographer.
Listed as a charter member of the National Photographic Association. PP, July 1869.

PHILLIPS, JOHN D., photographer.
4 Lexington (1870-1871); 255 Light (1882). CD, BD.

PHILLIPS, THOMAS, daguerreotype experimenter.
Noted as assisting James Green with the first experiments with the daguerreotype in Baltimore. BA, October 31, 1839.

PHIPPS, FRANK M., photographer.
321 N. Gay (1903-1904). BD.

PHIPPS, M.E., ambrotypist, photographer.
465 W. Baltimore (1863-1865?). Imprint on carte de viste, AC.

PHIPPS, WILLIAM M., photographer.
Operator of the Central Photo Studio, 427 E. Baltimore (1894-1904). CD.

PHOTOGRAPHIC CLUB OF BALTIMORE CITY.
703 Madison Ave. (1898-1899). CD.

PIERCY, JOHN H., photographer.
Born in Maryland, 1845; Piercy & Crosby, over 123 W. Baltimore (1874-1878); John Piercy only (1878-1881); over 101 N. Gay (1879-1881). CD.

PINDELL, EDWARD A., daguerreotypist.
and Howell, 105 W. Baltimore (1856-1857). CD.

PLUMBE, JOHN, daguerreotypist, publisher, entrepreneur.
Plumbe's National Gallery, corner North & Baltimore (November 1843-1846); 205 Baltimore (1846-1847). TS, CD.

PLUMLEY, HARRY A., photographer.
306 W. Lexington (1899). CD.

PLUMLEY, JOHN A., photographer.
588 N. Gay (1903); 1801 N. Fulton Ave. (1904). CD.

POHL, GERHART, photographer.
208 S. Bond (1858-1859). CD.

POLITZER, IGNATZ, photographer.
427 W. Baltimore (1863-1869). CD.

Gallery of John H. Pope at 91 W. Baltimore Street. Note the sidewalk showcases containing examples of his work. T. P. Varley's studio was next-door to the right. Author's collection

POLLOCK, HENRY, daguerreotypist, ambrotypist, photographer.
Born Washington D.C., 1810; $2000 capital invested; 250 plates on hand; 1 male employee; $50 ave. monthly labor cost; 5500 likenesses produced annually; 147 Lexington (1849-1850); 155 Baltimore (1850-1867); 44 Lexington (1868-1886); 9 E. Lexington (1887-1889). "None of the Daguerreotypists of Balto. except Pollock, are considered worthy of confidence or credit. They are generally an unreliable and irresponsible set of men who spend faster than they make, would not credit any of them (except the one named)..." U.S.C. 1860, U.S.M.C. 1860. TS, CD, DC (Maryland, Vol. 8, p. 519). (see biography)

POMERANETZ, JERONIM, photographer.
924 E. Baltimore (1899). CD.

POPE, JOHN H., photographer.
Born in Maryland, 1827; $4000 value of real estate, $1600 value of personal estate; over 91 W. Baltimore (1866-1873); and 123 W. Baltimore (1868-1869); 103 W. Baltimore (1874); 211 W. Baltimore (1875). U.S.C. 1870, CD.

PORTER, WILLIAM SOUTHGATE, daguerreotypist.
Gallery in the Franklin Buildings, NE. corner North & Baltimore (May 20, 1846-1848); to Cincinnati, Ohio (1848). TS, CD, AD.

POWELL, JOHN J., photographer, dealer in photographic supplies.
425 E. Baltimore (1894-1898); Powell & Mueller (1897). CD.

POWERS, MARCELLAS, photographer.
Born in Virginia, 1836. U.S.C. 1860.

PRATT, A.W., daguerreotypist.
Mentioned in advertisement for Cooke's 25 cents Gallery that he was employed as an operator after previously working in French's Gallery, Boston. TS, January 26, 1854.

PRICE, ___________, daguerreotypist.
211 Baltimore (ca. 1850). Imprint on velvet of miniature daguerreotype case, PC.

PRINCE, ROBERT E., photographer.
21 W. Lexington (1899); 713 Light & 861 N. Howard (1902-1903); 861 N. Howard (1903); 2936 York Rd. (1904). CD, BD.

PROCTOR, JAMES H., photographer.
Born in Maryland, 1848; living in the 7th Ward; 163 N. Gay (1882-1884); Proctor and Finley, 409 N. Gay (1887); J.H. Proctor only (1888); and Finley, 417 E. Baltimore (1889); 829 N. Gay (1894-1903). U.S.C. 1880, CD.

PROCTOR, RACHAEL, photographer.
829 N. Gay (1903). CD.

PURCELL, C.W., daguerreotypist.
Former operator for Broadbent & Carey, 128 Baltimore (1849-1850).
BA, November 12, 1849.

PURETZ, SOLOMON, photographer.
111 E. Baltimore (1897). CD.

****

QUARTLEY, CHARLES, photographer.
217 W. Baltimore (1878-1886); 11 E. Baltimore (1887-1904). CD.

****

RABENAU, DANIEL, daguerreotypist.
Over 127 W. Baltimore (1858-1859). CD.

RABEMAN, DANIEL, ambrotypist, photographer.
65 W. Baltimore (1858-1860). CD, BD.

RALEY, WALTER, photographer.
85 W. Baltimore (ca. 1865). Imprint on a tintype, AC.

REDINGTON, D.C., photographer.
Office- Wolle's Hotel, Nos. 3, 5, and 7 N. Eutaw (ca. 1875).
Imprint on a cabinet card, AC.

REISSERT & ARMIGER, photographers.
305 S. Broadway (1900). CD.

REINHART, H.J., photographer.
Born in Maryland, 1851; living in the 9th Ward. U.S.C. 1870.

REMHARDT, HENRY, photographer.
Born in Maryland, 1850; living in the 20th Ward. U.S.C. 1870.

REPSON, HARRY A., photographer.
508 S. Broadway (1896-1898). CD.

RIDDLE, A.J., daguerreotypist.
163 N. Gay (1851). TS.

RIDGELY, RICHARD D., photographer.
NE. corner Eutaw & Lexington (ca. 1863-1864); SE. corner Eutaw & Lexington (1864-1869). Imprint on carte de visite, AC, CD.

ROBINSON, ___________, daguerreotypist.
112 Baltimore (1844). TS, May 29, 1844.

ROBINSON, G.W., dealer of photographers' stock.
103 W. Baltimore (1877-1878). CD.

ROBINSON, HENRY B., daguerreotypist.
Dallas, south of Madison which was probably not a studio (1853-54). CD.

ROBINSON, J.C., daguerreotypist.
City Daguerrian Gallery, 211 Baltimore (1846-1847).
BA, December 25, 1846.

ROBINSON, MARTIN L., photographer.
Born in Pennsylvania, 1848; over 4 N. Green (1872); 468 W. Baltimore (1873-1875); 472 W. Baltimore (1877-1881); NE. corner Eutaw & Lexington (1882-1886); 1021 Harlem Avenue (1887); Eutaw corner Lexington (1888); 330 W. Lexington (1889-1895); 201 N. Eutaw (1894); 319 N. Paca (1896); 411 W. Fayette (1897-1898). U.S.C. 1870, CD.

> M. L. Robinson, Photographer, Northeast corner of Eutaw and Lexington Streets.- The gallery of Mr. M. L. Robinson has been in successful operation since 1871. A large trade has been built up extending to all parts of Maryland, and the returns of business are undergoing steady increase. The premises occupied comprise the whole of the third floor. The arrangement is both attractive and convenient. Photography is done in all its branches, and the highest standard of excellence is maintained. The policy followed by Mr. Robinson is to furnish the best productions at the lowest possible cost. The pictures and other work coming from this gallery are noted for their truthfulness to nature, and in this respect are not excelled by those of any similar concern in the country. They combine all desireable points of superiority, and the effects are brilliant and lasting. Mr. Robinson has resided in Baltimore for thirty-two years, and is a well-known and responsible man. HCP.

ROETH, WILLIAM, photographer.
Born in Maryland, 1853; living in the 17th Ward. U.S.C. 1870.

ROGERS, ALBERT L., photographer.
68 Lexington (1882-1885); "Successor to Busey," 112 N. Charles (1891). CD, imprint on cabinet card, AC.

ROGERS & WING, photographers.
17 S. Howard (ca. 1875). Imprint on a carte de visite, AC.

ROONEY, FRANCIS A., photographer.
"The Beehive Photograph Gallery," 127 Baltimore (1875); 19 E. Baltimore (1877-1886); Rooney & Walter (1878-1879). BCU, CD.

ROONEY, FRANK A., photographic studio manager.
Mentioned as manager of the New York Photo Co., 425 E. Baltimore (ca. 1885). Imprint on a cabinet card, AC.

ROONEY, J. HENRY, photographer.
Born in Maryland, 1848; 73 W. Baltimore (1880-1886); 417 E. Baltimore (1887-1888). U.S.C. 1880, CD.

ROOT, C.S., daguerreotypist.
SE. corner Baltimore & South (1849-1850). CD.

ROSEMAN, GEORGE W. JR., photographer.
Born in Maryland, 1852; 472 W. Baltimore (1873-1874). U.S.C. 1870, CD.

ROYER, SAMUEL L., photographer.
588 N. Gay (1899-1900); Royer & Laurent (1899). CD.

ROYS, ADOLPH V., photographer.
515 S. Broadway (1893-1895). CD.

RUCKLE, MRS. THOMAS C., daguerreotypist.
207 1/2 Baltimore (1848); "Thomas C. Ruckle has established the Lawrence Daguerrean Gallery in a room adjoining his Painting Room, which will be conducted by Mrs. Ruckle, under his immediate supervision." TS, October 27, 1848.

RUDOLPH, ERNEST, photographer.
Born in Saxony, 1861; 644 W. Baltimore (1887); 646 W. Baltimore (1888); 644 W. Baltimore (1889). U.S.C. 1880, CD.

RUFF, RICHARD H., daguerreotypist, ambrotypist, stereographer.
147 E. Baltimore (1856-1857); 19 W. Baltimore (1858). CD, BD.

RUSSELL & CO., photographers.
17 & 203 W. Lexington (1888); 5 N. Charles (1889). CD.

RUSSELL, BERNARD J. JR., photographer.
330 N. Gay (1900-1902); 952 W. Franklin (1903-1904). CD.

RUSSELL, WILLIAM C., photographer.
151 W. Fayette, (1886); 106 N. Charles (1887). CD.

RUSSELL, MRS. WILLIAM C. (DORA), photographer.
109 W. Lexington (1894-1901); 231 W. Lexington (1902-1904). CD.

****

SALGUES & CO., photographers.
105 W. Baltimore (1863-1864). CD.

SANDER, JACOB, photographer.
Born in Virginia, 1861; living in the 13th Ward. U.S.C. 1880.

SAVAGE & HUZZA, photographers.
German St., corner of Sharp St. (1864-1866). Imprint on CDV, PC.

SCHAEFER, FREDERICK, apprentice to photographer.
Born in Maryland, 1864; son of John Henry Schaefer; living in the 14th Ward. U.S.C. 1880.

SCHAEFER, HENRY. apprentice to photographer.
Born in Germany, 1864; living in the 17th Ward. U.S.C. 1880.

SCHAEFER, J. HENRY, photographer.
Born in Hesse Darmstadt, 1830; 671 W. Baltimore (1863-1868); 643 W. Baltimore (1870-1886); 887 W. Baltimore (1887-1904), and Son (1896-1904). U.S.C. 1880, CD. (see Maryland Counties)

> J. Henry Schaefer, Gallery of Artistic Photography, No. 887 West Baltimore Street, near Poppleton Street.- This is one of old-established art studios of Baltimore, the business having been inaugurated by the present proprietor in 1860 at the present eligible location. Mr. Schaefer is an artist of decided skill and genius. His rooms are very elegantly arranged and appointed for his purposes, and his facilities for first-class work are unsurpassed. He is famous for the beautiful Rembrandt and artistic effects of his work. He makes photographs in all the latest styles of the art, and gives particular attention to the copying and enlarging of all kinds of pictures. He carries in stock and makes to order all kinds of frames, and in all his dealings he is thoroughly reliable, prompt, and obliging. For first-class, meritorious work, Mr. Schaefer's prices are the lowest in the city. Mr. Schaefer is a native of the Fatherland, and has resided in the United States for thirty-five years. HCP.

SCHAEFER, JAMES, photographer.
50 N. Liberty (1882). CD.

SCHAEFER, WILLIAM, photographer.
Born in Maryland, 1862; son of John Henry Schaefer;
643 W. Baltimore (1882-1883). U.S.C. 1880, CD.

SCHNELL, C., photographer.
464 W. Baltimore (1858). BD.

SCHUTTE (SCHUETTE), H. JR., photographer.
Over 20 N. Charles (1882-1883); 123 S. Broadway (1885); and Co. (1882); 23 N. Washington (1886); Eagle Photo and Viewing Co., 113 N. Washington (ca. 1886). CD, imprint on cabinet card, AC.

SCHUTTE, HARRY B., photographer.
113/423 (renumbered) N. Washington (1887). CD.

SCHUTTE, HENRY B., photographer.
423 N. Washington (1888-1889, 1895-1904); 425 N. Washington (1894). CD.

SCHWAMB, CHARLES A., photographer.
159 W. Baltimore (1859-1860). BD, CD.

SCHWEIKERT, JOHN R., photographer.
465 W. Baltimore (1874-1875). CD.

SCHWEIKERT & MACKE, photographers.
300 N. Gay (1873). CD.

SCOTT, EDWARD R., daguerreotypist.
85 Baltimore (1854); 87 Baltimore (1855-1856).
TS, January 22, 1854, CD.

SEIXEAS (SEIXAS), ___________, daguerreotypist.
Pioneer daguerrean who exhibited the first daguerreotypes in Baltimore and demonstrated its procedures. TS, April 1840.

SELANDER & ENGEL, photographers.
754 W. Baltimore (1902-1903). BD.

SELANDER, CHARLES J., photographer.
1828 Orleans (1901); 2104 E. Fayette (1902); 644 W. Baltimore (1903); 114 W. Lexington (1904). CD.

SELANDER, JULIUS, photographer.
1710 Eastern Ave. (1888-1889); 1827 Orleans (1898); 1828 Orleans (1900). CD.

SELBY & DULANEY, booksellers, stationers, dealers in photographers.
332 W. Baltimore (1867-1870). CD.

SELBY & McCAULEY, sellers of photographic albums and cartes de visite.
32 W. Baltimore (1864); 36 W. Baltimore (1865-1866). CD.

SELBY, JOHN T., photographer.
501 N. Eutaw & 323 W. Lexington (1902); 323 W. Lexington (1903-1904). CD.

SHAW, ___________, operator in the gallery of P.L. Perkins.
"Mr. Shaw, who has been operating at this establishment, is a good workman and fully understands his business." PFAJ, 1857.

SHAW, W., photographer.
S. Holliday near Fayette (1858-1859). CD.

SHEW, JACOB, daguerreotypist.
Manager of John Plumbe's National Gallery in Baltimore (1843?-April 1846); 117 Baltimore (May 1846-1850); Shew and Marks (1848-1850); Marks assumed control of the studio by April 1850 after Shew departed to open gallery with brother Myron in Philadelphia. Traveled to California in 1854 where he opened a studio in Sacremento. CD, TS, AD. (see H.R. Marks)

SHIPLEY, ELMER E.A., photographer.
214 N. Eutaw (1899). CD.

SHOREY, WILLIAM F., photographer.
Born in Maine, 1833; 87 W. Baltimore (1864-1866); 105 W. Baltimore (1867-1878); 157 W. Baltimore (1879-1886); 131 E. Baltimore (1887-1894); and 129 E. Baltimore (1889, 1891). CD. (see biography)

SHRIVER & RICKARDS, photographers.
746 W. Baltimore (1900). CD.

SHULMAN, NATHAN, photographer.
Born in 1870 in Pinsk, Russia; entered the photographic profession as a photographer's assistant in Pinsk before opening his own studio in Mozyr; emigrated to the U.S. in 1897 where he took up a position in the photography studio of Gimbel's Department Store in New York; moved to Baltimore in 1898 to open a studio at 924 E. Baltimore Street and soon occupied the entire building; became the leading photographer for the medical and business community after his "discovery" by Daniel Gilman, president of Johns Hopkins University; opened an additional studio on Noth Charles Street just before World War I; died September 27, 1917. Maryland Bicentennial Jewish Book, 1975.

SHULTZ, CHARLES E., photographer.
1030 Pennsylvania Ave. (1898); 501 Oliver Place (1899). CD.

SIEGFRIED, __________, daguerreotypist.
19 E. Baltimore (1855); advertised that he was "Late of Mr. Walzl's." TS, February 22, 1855.

SIEKER BROS., photographers.
Over 123 W. Baltimore (1873). CD.

SIEWERD, LOUIS H., photographer.
15 Clay (1900). CD.

SIMONS & WOLCOTT, daguerreotypists.
199 W. Baltimore (1845). CD.

SITES, HARRY, photographer.
1121 Argyle Ave. (1902); 11 E. Baltimore (1902-1903);
1626 Argyle Ave. (1903). CD, BD.

SKINNER, JOHN C., photographer.
578 W. Baltimore (1867-1868); 472 W. Baltimore (1870-1871); and Co. (1867-1868). CD, BD.

SLINCHCOMB, CHARLES, photographer.
Born in Maryland, 1840; living in the 14th Ward. U.S.C. 1870.

SMITH & CO., photographers.
130 Gough (1881). CD.

SMITH & ERNSBERGER, photographers, photo-copiers.
21 Orleans (1883-1885). CD.

SMITH, AARON, photographer.
924 E. Baltimore (1898). CD.

SMITH, E.M., photographer.
65 Fulton (ca. 1866). Imprint on a tintype, AC.

SMITH, JOHN T., photographer.
1030 Pennsylvania Ave. (1903). CD.

SMITH, T.O., daguerreotypist.
Mentioned as the former principal operator of Root's Gallery in Philadelphia, he was employed in Solomon N. Carvalho's Gallery of Fine Arts, 205 Baltimore, where he was to "attend to the production of an entirely new style of Daguerreotype, patented under the name of the Crayon Daguerreotype, never introduced into this city. The great advantage which this style of picture possesses over any other, is that the picture can be seen equally well in any light, and as distinctly when hung against a wall as

the finest miniature. The whole strength of the Instrument is thrown on the head, and the artistic distribution of light and shadow give it the appearance of one of the celebrated Italian Crayon Drawings." BA, May 28, 1849. (see Solomon N. Carvalho)

SMITH, WILLIAM H., photographer, photo-copying.
501 N. Gay (1886); 1123 Orleans (1887); 810 N. Gay (1896). CD.

SOPER, HERBERT W. CO. (THE), dealer of photographic supplies.
223 Park Ave. (1899). CD.

SOUTH, J.M., photographer.
109 Lexington (1877-1878). BD, CD.

SOUTHERN PUBLISHING CO., photographic publishers.
135 W. Baltimore (1862-1865?). Imprint on CDV, PC.

SPEAT, GEORGE, photographer.
116 S. Broadway (1886). CD.

SPEDDEN, WILLIAM L., photographer.
65 W. Baltimore (1870-1871); 73 W. Baltimore (1874-1875). CD.

SPEIGHTS, JOHN S. (WINAN GALLERY), photographer.
560 W. Baltimore (Oct. 1859-1860). TS, BD, CD.

SPICER, FRANK H., photographer.
Born in Maryland, 1841; 300 N. Gay (1874-1877). U.S.C. 1880, CD.

SPRIGGS & MESKE, dealers of daguerreotype cases & materials.
Mentioned in an advertisement to be located at 35 Baltimore.
TS, February 23, 1849.

STAHN, MATTHEW (MATHIAS), ambrotypist, photographer.
Born in Prussia, 1820; 91 N. Gay (1863-1864); 87 N. Gay (1865-1886); 227 N. Gay (1887); 229 N. Gay (1888-1895).
U.S.C. 1870, BD, CD.

STANTON & BUTLER, photographers.
79 W. Fayette (1867-1868); 14 N. Charles (1870-1871). CD.

STARR, JAMES, daguerreotypist.
Born Maryland, 1838; living in the 10th Ward. U.S.C. 1860.

STAUM, ELVIN E., "Artistic Photographer."
1425 W. Saratoga (1903); 913 Appleton (1904). CD.

STEHL (STEEL), BERNARD G., photographer.
357 W. Baltimore (1867-1869). CD.

STEVENS, A.L., daguerreotypist.
Advertisement for gallery on corner of Broadway & Eastern Ave.
TS, September 27, 1854.

STEVENSON, JOHN G., daguerreotypist.
Advertisement for his arrival in Baltimore to make "Daguerreotype Likenesses." BA, October 14, 1840.

STEWART, JOSEPH T., photographer.
427 E. Baltimore (1896). CD.

STILTZ, D.R., daguerreotypist, photographer.
159 W. Baltimore (1856-1857); 82 S. Sharp (1858-1859); 244 Baltimore (1859); "View Photographers, office at Butler, Perrigo & Way's, 108 W. Baltimore, upstairs" (1864); Williamsport, Pa. (1875); former operator for J.H. Whitehurst. CD, TS, imprint on carte de visite, AC, PP.

STOWELL, J. WILLIAM, photographer.
9 1/2 W. Baltimore (1879-1880). CD.

SUSSMAN, J. PHOTO STOCK CO. (THE)
223 Park Ave. (1900-1904). CD.

SWEET, WILLIAM H., photographer.
11 W. Baltimore (1859-1860); over 147 Lexington (1864);
203 W. Pratt (1865-1868). CD, BD.

SZABO, SAMUEL G., daguerreotypist.
Boarding at 29 Holliday (1858). CD.

****

TAGART, HENRY, photographer.
249 S. Broadway (1880). CD.

TANQUEREY ART STUDIO, photographers.
21 E. Baltimore (ca. 1880). Imprint on cabinet cards, AC.

TATUM, J.H., photographic inventor.
Received patent no. 14,679 on April 15, 1856 for a process for "Preparation of oil ground to receive Photographic Impressions." PR.

TAYLOR, __________, ambrotypist, photographer.
"Taylor's New Photograph and Ambrotype Gallery, no. 217 Baltimore st., near Charles, over Mr. Balge's Jewelry Store."
TS, February 18, 1861.

TAYLOR, GEORGE W.H., photographer.
147 W. Lexington (1860-1867); was a former employee of J.D. Marsters and took over his gallery by November 1860.
TS, November 9, 1860, BD, CD.

TAYLOR, JOHN, photographic copier.
22 E. Lombard (1885). CD.

THOMAS, EDWIN, daguerreotypist.
Over 125 Baltimore (1849-1850). CD.

THOMLINSON & PARDRE, daguerreotypists.
Advertisement for gallery at 10 N. Charles. TS, April 26, 1845.

THOMPSON, CONRAD J., photographer.
113 N. Washington (1885); 1047 W. Saratoga (1887); 1303 N. Fulton (1888). CD.

TORSCH, HENRY F. JR., photographer.
51 N. Eutaw (1870-1871); 280 W. Baltimore (1872-1873). BD.

TOWSON & PROCTOR, photographers.
163 N. Gay (1880-1886). CD.

TRAINOR STUDIO, photographers.
NE. corner Eutaw & Lexington (ca. 1880). Imprint on cabinet card, AC.

TRAINOR, JAMES B., photographer.
731 W. Baltimore (1888-1904). CD.

TRAINOR, MARTIN D., photographer.
45 Argyle Ave. (1885-1886); 731 W. Baltimore (1889, 1894); 427 E. Baltimore (1890-1891); 201 N. Eutaw (1896-1904). CD.

TROPPMAN, H., photographer.
61 Hanover (1863-1864). CD.

TUCKER, JOSEPH, daguerreotypist.
Born Washington, D.C., 1797; 131 1/2 W. Baltimore (1855-1857); 465 W. Baltimore (1858-1864); 466 W. Baltimore (1863-1864). U.S.C. 1860, CD, BD.

TUCKER, WESLEY A., daguerreotypist.
Born Maryland, 1828; $500 invested; 200 plates on hand; 2 male employees; $60 average monthly labor cost; 2000 likenesses produced annually. U.S.C. 1850, U.S.M.C. 1850.

TUCKER, WILLIAM A., daguerreotypist.
101 Baltimore (1853). CD.

TURNER, M., photographer?
Listed as agent for the Southern Photographic Temple of Art, 213 Baltimore St. TS, April 13, 1858.

TURNER, T.C.S., photographer.
213 W. Baltimore (1859-1860). BD.

TUTTLE, E., photographer, ambrotypist.
207 Baltimore (1858). BD.

****

VALENTINE, ___________, daguerreotypist.
Mentioned as the principal operator at the gallery of Woodbridge & Harris. TS, January 5, 1854.

VANDEFORD, ABEL, photographer.
Born in Maryland, 1846; living in the 17th Ward. U.S.C. 1880.

VANDERFORD (VANDAFOARD), ABRAM J., photographer.
19 E. Baltimore (1875); 73 W. Baltimore (1877-1880). CD.

VAN GANTT, T., daguerreotypist.
Operator for J. H. Whitehurst. PP.

VAN NESS, CHARLES W., photographer.
159 W. Baltimore (1865-1866); 85 W. Baltimore (1867); SE. corner Gay & Chestnut (1868-1869); 26 N. Gay (1870-1871). CD.

VAN WAGNER & DYER, photographers.
468 W. Baltimore (1871). CD.

VAN WAGNER, J.M., photographer.
Born in New York, 1843; living in the 14th Ward. U.S.C. 1870.

VARDEN & LANSDALE, photographers.
Over 220 W. Baltimore (1863-1864). CD.

VARLEY, THOMAS P., photographer.
Over 93 W. Baltimore (1867-1868); over SE. corner Baltimore & Holliday (1868-1870); 155 W. Baltimore (1871-1873);
157 W. Baltimore (1874-1877). CD.

VITEK, ANTON, photographer.
930 N. Broadway (1902). CD.

VOLKMAN, CHARLES, photographer.
6 N. Frederick (1863-1864). CD.

****

WAGNER, ADOLPH, photographer.
Born in Maryland, 1855; son of Ferdinand Wagner; living in the 9th Ward. U.S.C. 1880.

WAGNER & MAIER, photographers.
Over 439 W. Baltimore (1871-1872). CD.

WAGNER, CHARLES A., photographer.
65 W. Baltimore (1884-1886); 425 E. Baltimore (1887). CD.

WAGNER, F.W. & CO., dealer of photographic supplies.
5 W. Lexington (1898-1904). CD.

WAGNER, FERDINAND, ambrotypist.
Born in France, 1840; gallery located in the 6th Ward. U.S.C. 1860.

WAGNER, FERDINAND, daguerreotypist, photographer.
Born in Prussia, 1819; 300 N. Gay (1858-1859); 63 W. Baltimore (1863-1886); 427 E. Baltimore (1887-1889); 419 E. Baltimore (1894-1904); and Son (1874-1904). U.S.C. 1870, CD.

WAGNER, HENRY, daguerreotypist, photographer.
$300 capital invested; 1 male employee; $60 average monthly labor cost; 3000 likenesses produced yearly valued at $1600; 220 Light (1858-1864). U.S.M.C. 1860, CD.

WAGNER, JOHN M., photographer.
327 N. Gay (1900-1903); 424 E. Preston (1904). CD.

WALLER, F., photographer.
Operator in the gallery of Richard Walzl; author of numerous technical articles in Walzl's magazine <u>The Photographer's Friend</u>. PF, 1874.

WALTER & PIERCY, photographers.
101 N. Gay (1877-1878). CD.

WALTER, CHARLES T., photographer.
9 E. Lexington (1896-1904); proprietor of the American View Co., 288 N. Charles (1900-1904). CD, BD.

WATERS, JAMES S., bookseller, dealer in photographs.
168 W. Baltimore (1864); 6 N. Charles (1865-1866); and Son (George F.), 8 N. Charles (1867-1870); 170 W. Fayette (1872-1873). CD.

WALTERS, WILLIAM H., photographer.
100 N. Wolfe (1898). CD.

WALZL, JOHN H., daguerreotypist, photographer, photographic supplies dealer.
63 Baltimore (1854-1860); and 19 E. Baltimore (1856-1860); over 213 W. Baltimore (September 1860-1864); dealer in photographic stock, 25 Holliday (1867-1868); over 77 W. Baltimore (1868-1869). TS, CD, BD. (see biography)

WALZL, JOHN T., photographer.
Born in Maryland, 1860; son of Louis Walzl; 508 S. Broadway (1887, 1889). U.S.C. 1880, CD.

WALZL, LOUIS, ambrotypist, photographer.
Born in Vienna, 1837; 93 Baltimore (Sept. 1857-1860); 91 Baltimore (April 1860- Fall 1862); over 65 W. Baltimore (1862-1864); over 77 W. Baltimore (1867-1869); 9 N. Washington (1870-1876); 157 S. Broadway (1880-1881); 9 N. Washington (1882-1883, 1885-1886); 157 S. Broadway (1884). U.S.C. 1860, CD.

WALZL, LOUIS, photographer.
Born in Maryland, 1863; son of Louis Walzl (above); living in the 1st Ward. U.S.C. 1880.

WALZL, RICHARD, ambrotypist, photographer, publisher, photographic entrepreneur.
Born in Vienna, 1844; 77 W. Baltimore (1862-1867); and 75 W. Baltimore (1865- June 28, 1866 when the studio was struck by fire); 103 W. Baltimore (September 2, 1866-1872); 46 N. Charles (1873-1881); 205 W. Baltimore (1882-1886); 21 E. Baltimore (1887-1890); and 501 N. Eutaw (1888-1890); Franklin, corner Eutaw (1891-1893); 501 N. Eutaw (1894-1898). CD, U.S.C. 1860, BC. (see biography)

WALZL, SIDNEY E., photographic agent, dealer in photographic supples.
Son of John H. Walzl, possible cousin of Richard Walzl; advertised as an agent for the studio in the Marble Building, NE. corner Eutaw and Franklin (ca. 1891-1893); Photographic Supplies and Art Production, 20 W. Lexington (1904). Imprint on advertising card, CD. (see John H. & Richard Walzl)

WAMPLER, JAMES F., photographer.
Born in the District of Columbia, 1853; 472 W. Baltimore (ca. 1870). U.S.C. 1870, imprint on carte de visite, AC. (see Maryland Counties)

WARNER, CHRISTOPHER, photographer.
73 W. Baltimore (1875). CD.

WEAVER, E.J., photographer.
147 E. Baltimore (1871). BD.

WEAVER, HARRY B., photographer.
1151 E. Baltimore (1889-1904). CD.

WEAVER, HARRY B., photographer.
85 W. Baltimore (1863-1864). CD.

WEAVER, JOHN, photographer.
Born in Maryland, 1858; son of William H. Weaver; living in the 4th Ward. U.S.C. 1880.

WEAVER, WILLIAM H., photographer, artist.
Born December 1827, died October 8, 1913; 147 E. Baltimore (1863-1886); & Son, 1151 E. Baltimore (1894-1895). CD, BA July 11, 1886, BD.

WEEDEN, E.B., daguerreotypist.
Advertisement for gallery "next door to Dr. Mokur" in East Baltimore. TS, October 21, 1854.

WEILEPP, AUGUST, photographer.
19 E. Baltimore (1862-1871). Dated CDV, AC, CD.

WELDEN, HOLHAM F., daguerreotypist.
Born in Maryland, 1813; living in 4th Ward. U.S.C. 1860.

WELDEN, W.T., photographer.
65 W. Baltimore (1867-1869). CD.

WELDEN, WILLIAM F., daguerreotypist.
Born in Maryland, 1843; living in the 7th Ward. U.S.C. 1860.

WERSMAN, JOHN, photographer.
Born in Pennsylvania, 1848; living in the 8th Ward. U.S.C. 1870.

WERTHEIM, ALPHONESE, photographer.
21 E. Baltimore (1894-1895). CD.

WEST, GEORGE F., photographic sales.
9 E. Lexington (ca. 1880). Imprint on a magic lantern slide, PC.

Gallery of William H. Weaver at 147 E. Baltimore Street. Maryland Historical Society Collection

WHEEDON, EUGENE BEAUHARNIAS, daguerreotypist, ambrotypist.
135 S. Broadway (1856-1859); and 464 W. Baltimore (1856-1857); corner Broadway & Bank (1859); and Son (1856-1859). BD, CD, TS, September 23, 1859.

WHEEDEN, MADISON (AND SON), photographer.
135 S. Broadway (1859-1869); 133 S. Broadway (1870-1874); and Son (1860-1874). BD, CD.

WHITEHILL, LOUIS, daguerreotypist.
163 N. Gay (1856-1859); 282 N. Gay (1863-1864); 300 N. Gay (1871). CD, BD.

WHITEHURST, JESSE, daguerreotypist, photographer, entreprenuer.
Born in Virginia, 1823; $6000 invested; 500 plates on hand, 6 male employees; $184 average monthly labor cost; 6500 likenesses produced yearly; 207 1/2 Baltimore (1849-1851); 205 Baltimore (July 1851- September 1857); 213 Baltimore (October 1857-April 1860); 123 Baltimore (May 1860-1864). U.S.C. 1870, U.S.M.C. 1850, TS, CD. (see biography)

WILDE, JOHN, ambrotypist.
Born in Maryland, 1805; value of personal property $1500. U.S.C. 1860.

WILDE, J.F.W., daguerreotypist.
43 Hampstead Rd. which was probably a residence (1851-1854). CD.

WILDE, JOHN T., ambrotypist.
Born in Maryland, 1840; value of personal property $200. U.S.C. 1860.

WILKES, D.G., photographer.
Born in England, 1850; living in the 9th Ward. U.S.C. 1880.

WILKES, DAVID J., photographer.
Born in Maryland, 1850; "Successor to W.L. Spedden," 65 W. Baltimore (1872); 63 & 125 W. Baltimore (1873); over 125 W. Baltimore (1874-1885); over 137 W. Baltimore (1886); 211 E. Baltimore (1887-1896, 1898-1904); 213 E. Baltimore (1897). U.S.C. 1880, imprint on tintype, AC, CD.

WILLIAMS, JOHN T., daguerreotypist.
Over 211 Baltimore (1851); $1000 invested; 250 plates on hand; 2 male employees; $100 average monthly labor cost; 3000 likenesses produced annually. CD, U.S.M.C. 1850.

WILSON, __________, photographic colorist.
Mentioned as a "clever artist" who did photographic portraits in oil at the gallery of P.L. Perkins. PFAJ, 1857.

WILSON, CHARLES, photographer.
93 W. Baltimore (1863-1864). CD.

WILSON, CHARLES A., photographer, dealer in photographic stock.
Dinmore & Wilson, 125 W. Baltimore (1872); 7 N. Charles (1873-1875); Charles A. Wilson only (1874-1875). CD.

WILSON, JOSHUA H., photographer.
Mt. Winans (1894-1895); 420 E. Baltimore (1896-1904). CD.

WINCHESTER, O.F., daguerreotypist.
Advertisement for gallery at 163 Baltimore. TS, August 4, 1843.

WINTER, HENRY, photographer.
578 W. Baltimore (1865-1866). CD.

WISONG, WILLIAM A., artist, painters and daguerreotypists supplies.
2 N. Liberty (1847-1859); sold to Wm. King & Bro. (ca. 1860). CD.

WOLCOTT, WILLIAM K., daguerreotypist.
217 W. Baltimore (1845). CD.

WOODBRIDGE, JOHN J., daguerreotypist.
244 Baltimore (1854-1856); and Harris (1855-1856). TS, CD.

WOODWARD, DAVID, artist, inventor, writer.
Born Philadelphia, September 16, 1823, died November 29, 1909; Received patent no. 16,700 on February 24, 1857 for a "Solar Camera;" received patent no. 31,639 on March 5, 1861 for a "mode of operating the reflectors of Solar Cameras". PR.
(see biography)

WORLD PHOTO CO. (THE)
9 E. Lexington (1893). CD.

WUNDER, FRANK J., photographer.
219 N. Eutaw (1897-1904). CD.

WUNDER, GEORGE, photographer.
333 W. Baltimore (1863-1864, 1867-1868). CD.

WUNDER, GEORGE, photographer.
Born in Maryland, 1825; 483 W. Baltimore (1867-1869); 478 W. Baltimore (1874-1877); 482 W. Baltimore (1878-1879); 51 N. Eutaw (1880-1885); 271 Hollins (1886). CD, BD.

WUNDER, MARY A., photographer.
219 N. Eutaw (1887); 217 N. Eutaw (1888-1894); 219 N. Eutaw (1895-1896). CD.

****

YOUNG, JOHN H., photographer.
Born in Pennsylvania, 1832; cor. Light & Baltimore (1859); over SW. corner Baltimore & Charles and over SW. corner Light & Baltimore (1860); 231 W. Baltimore (1862); 205 & 231 W. Baltimore (1863); over SW. corner Baltimore & Charles and 205 W. Baltimore (1864); over 465 W. Baltimore (1867-1870). BD, dated CDV, AC, CD.

YUNG, SUSAN, assists photographer.
Born in Maryland, 1859; living in the 17th Ward. U.S.C. 1880.

****

ZOLLINHOFER, JAMES C., photographer.
21 W. Lexington (1896-1898). CD.

****

ANDERSON, EDWARD H., photographer.
Easton, Talbot Co. (1866). SD.

ARMINGER, B.W., photographer.
Havre de Grace, Harford Co. (ca. 1890). Imprint on cabinet card, AC. (see Baltimore City)

****

BACHRACH, DAVID, photographer.
& W. M. Chase, Naval Academy, Annapolis, Anne Arundel Co. (1868).

BAIRD, J.N., photographer.
Easton, Talbot Co. (1871). SD.

BALDWIN, JOHN W., photographer.
Successor to T.O. Cooper, over Boyles Drug Store, Westminster, Carroll Co. (1891-1906). SD.

BARNES, ROBERT & WESLEY F., photographers.
Porters, Carroll Co. (1891-1897). SD.

BARRY, ALONZO L., photographer.
Port Deposit, Cecil Co. (1871-1901). SD.

BELL, EMERICK C., photographer.
Hagerstown, Washington Co. (1891-1901). SD.

BELL, W.C., photographer.
Frederick, Frederick Co. (1891-1901). SD.

BENNEISEN & Bro., photographers.
Unionville, Frederick Co. (1880). SD.

BISHOP, W.N. and H.T., photographers.
Post Office Building, Cumberland, Allegany Co. (ca. 1880). Imprint on a carte de visite, AC.

BLESSING, J.P., photographer.
Brownsville, Washington Co. (1899-1901). SD. (see Baltimore City)

BOBLITZ, E.L., photographer.
Mechanicstown, Frederick Co. (1880, 1882). SD.

BRIGGS, ISAAC, itinerant daguerreotypist.
Learned the daguerreotype process from Henry Pollock in April 1848 (see Baltimore City); made daguerreotypes in Union Bridge, New Windsor, Sandy Spring, and Rockville (April 1849-May 1850) before traveling on to Virginia. MHS.

BROOKE, FRANKLIN, photographer.
Oakland, Garrett Co. (1887-1892). SD.

BROOKS, W.H., photographer.
Cumberland, Allegany Co. (1887). SD.

BROWN & CANNOLES, photographers.
Centerville, Queen Anne's Co. (1866). SD.

BROWN, GEORGE W., photographer.
No. 31 Broadway, Frostburg, Allegany Co. (ca. 1875). SD.
Imprint on cartes de visite, PC.

BROWN, GEORGE W.C., photographer.
Havre de Grace, Harford Co. (1894-1895). SD.
(see Baltimore City)

BROWN, JOHN H., photographer.
Colora, Cecil Co. (1894-1897). SD.

BROWN, V.O., itinerant daguerreotypist.
Westminster, Carroll Co. (ca. 1853).

BOUDISH, N.S., photographer.
U.S. Naval Academy, Annapolis, Anne Arundal Co. (ca. 1867).
Imprint on carte de visite, PC.

BOWES, P.S., daguerreotypist.
Hagerstown, Washington Co. (ca. 1850). Signed daguerreotype case, AC.

BURGER, C.E., photographer.
"Over Boyles Drug Store, successor to F.T. Castle," Westminster, Carroll Co. (ca. 1880). Imprint on cabinet card, PC.

BURGER, WILLIAM A., photographer.
Frederick, Frederick Co. (1880-1901). SD.

> Mr. Burger, whose Photography deserves special mention at our hands, is in every sense a competent, pains-taking artist; naturally adapted to the work in question, careful education to its intricacies, has developed the artist who comprehends the pose, the drapery, the every accessory which go to make up the portrait "a thing of beauty, a joy forever." The Gallery, of which Mr. Burger became the proprietor in 1875, succeeding J.R. Marken, at No. 23 North Market street, Frederick, is an old established one, but the art since then, and especially under the present management, has so advanced, the student of Daguerre who first "took pictures" would scarce (continued)

recognize the works of real art which now adorn the studio and parlors of Mr. Burger. A native of Frederick County, in which he all his life resided, doing fine and careful work, Mr. Burger is yet a pains-taking artist, and of course popular. Art and skill have done so much, that in the hands of such as he the production of the finished portrait is more like an exquisite steel engraving than aught else; nature is copied with a nicety of detail, a beauty and completeness, as wonderful as it is admirable. With nine years close application to his business, adopting the improvements in style, as well as the discoveries in the art as fast as they really prove themselves such, he has been able to build up his business to its present large and steadily increasing trade. MID.

BYERLY, CHARLES, photographer.
Frederick, Frederick Co. (1899-1901). SD. (see biography)

BYERLY, JACOB, daguerreotypist, ambrotypist, photographer.
Frederick, Frederick Co. (1842-1865); and Son (1866); $300 capital invested, 2 male employees, $60 average monthly labor cost, 1500 pictures produced annually with a $600 value. SD, U.S.M.C. 1860.

BYERLY, JOHN DAVIS, photographer.
29 North Market, Frederick, Frederick Co. (1871-1897). SD.

He is the worthy son and successor of the late Jacob Byerly, who was himself a student of the art, and who founded the present studio in 1842. Sixteen years later his son became proprietor, and the owner of the building which he now occupies. It is situated in the best possible location in Frederick City, has large, well lighted rooms, and possesses every advantage which modern invention can suggest.... Examination of his portraits shows a pleasing and agreeable variety-- the positions given have an ease and grace not often attained by photography, and in this, together with the admirable finish of his work, may be found the secret of Mr. B's great success. The Byerly Picture Gallery contains the result of an industry which is as interesting in its way as anything in the country, and fully as important. Every modern process known to the art, and tending toward its perfection is here employed, to meet all requirements of patrons, and the visitor that enters merely as an interested spectator, is as sure of courtesy and welcome, as if coming to spend money. By keeping pace with the times, Mr. Byerly has more than doubled his business, and now employs three skilled assistants in his different departments. He ensures, to all who try his skill, the most ample satisfaction. Special care is given to the portraits of children, and also to out and indoor work, landscape, etc. MID.

BYERS, WALTER H., photographer.
Hagerstown, Washington Co. (1899-1901). SD.

****

CASLER, M.M., photographer.
Annapolis, Anne Arundel Co. (1891-1892). SD.

CHANCE, JAMES, artist and photographer.
Annapolis, Anne Arundel Co. (1866-1880). SD.

CHOATE, SAMUEL C., photographer.
122 Baltimore Street, Cumberland, Allegany Co. (1891-1895). SD.

COLLIER, C.L., photographs and ambrotypes.
Elkton, Cecil Co. (1871). SD.

CONAWAY, WALTER, photographer.
Daniel, Carroll Co. (1899-1901). SD.

CONRAD, ELMER, photographer.
Frostburg, Allegany Co. (1887). SD.

COOPER, T.O., photographer.
Westminister, Carroll Co. (ca. 1885). Imprint on a cabinet card, AC.

CRAWFORD, R. CLAY, photographer.
Chestertown, Kent Co. (1869). PP.

CULBERTSON, WILLIAM, photographer.
Corner of Market & Patrick Streets, Frederick, Frederick Co. (ca. 1870). Imprint on a carte de visite, AC.

CULPEPPER, D.W., photographer.
Cambridge, Dorchester Co. (1866). SD.

****

DaCAMERA, J.B., photographer.
Westminster, Carroll Co. (1882). SD.

DARNELL, THOMAS L., photographer.
96 Baltimore, Cumberland, Allegany Co. (1871); and Son (1880- 1901). SD.

DAVIS, __________, photographer.
Federalsburg, Caroline Co. (ca. 1875). Imprint on cabinet card, AC.

DAY BROTHERS, photographers.
Havre de Grace, Harford Co. (ca. 1895). Imprint on cabinet card, AC.

DEDENHONER, WILLIAM, photographer.
Westminster, Carroll Co. (1871). SD.

DEILMAN, LEWIS, pharmacist and photographer.
New Windsor, Carroll Co. (1885-1900).

DUCKETT, G.W., photographer.
Jewell, Anne Arundel Co. (1887). SD.

****

EDWARDS, HENRY, photographer.
Smithsburg, Washington Co. (1899-1901). SD.

EVERHART GREENSBURY, W.J., photographer.
Manchester, Carroll Co. (1891-1901). SD.

EWING & CO., photographers.
Cumberland, Allegany Co. (1865-1866). Tax stamp on a CDV, PC, SD.

****

FICHTNER, J.M., photographer.
Cumberland, Allegany Co. (ca. 1866). Imprint on a CDV, AC.

FINLEY, C.E., photographer.
Cambridge, Dorchester Co. (1891-1901). SD.

FISCHNER, J.N., photographer.
Pocomoke City, Worcester Co. (1880). SD.

FLOWER, J.F., photographer.
Easton, Talbot Co. (1891-1892). SD.

FREEBURGER, WILLIAM H., photographer.
Ellicott City, Howard Co. (1894-1895). SD.

FREEBURGER & SON, photographers.
Salisbury, Wicomico Co. and Pocomoke City, Worcester Co. (ca. 1880). Imprint on carte de visite, AC.

FREEBURGER, WILLIAM H., photographer.
Ellicott City, Howard Co. (1894-1895). SD.

FREY & COOK, photographers.
Hancock, Washington Co. (ca. 1863). Imprint on carte de visite, PC.

FREY, D.R., photographer.
Wolfsville, Frederick Co. (1899-1901). SD.

****

GERKINS, C.E., photographer.
Lonaconing, Allegany Co. (1899-1901). SD.

GERMAN, JOSEPH, itinerant photographer.
Exhibited stereoscopic photographs of Towson and Baltimore City in the Baltimore County Court House. BCU, November 13, 1877.

GORDON, D.J., photographers.
Pocomoke City, Worcester Co. (1891-1897). SD.

GRAHAM, BENJAMIN, photographer.
Snow Hill, Worcester Co. (1866). SD.

GRAMMER, H.B., daguerreotypist, ambrotypist, photographer.
"Daguerrean Gallery, Ambrotype, Sphereotype, Melainotype, Carroll Hall," Westminster, Carroll Co. (1856, 1866); and Perkins (1867). AS, SD, imprint on carte de visite, AC.

GRUBER, F.D., photographer.
Hagerstown, Washington Co. (1896-1901). SD.

****

HAINES, NATHAN, plasterer & photographer.
Weldon, Frederick Co. (1899-1901). SD.

Portrait of H. B. Grammer. Tom Gordon, Jr. Collection

HARDING, EDWARD S., photographer.
Corner of Market and Patrick Streets, Frederick, Frederick Co. (ca. 1880). Imprint on carte de visite, AC.

HASKELL, H.M., photographer.
Weisesburgh, Baltimore Co. (1871). SD.

HAUGH, ___________, photographer.
York Road, Baltimore Co. (ca. 1880). Imprint on cabinet card, AC.

HAUGH, JOHN A., photographer.
Ladiesburg, Frederick Co. (1891-1901). SD.

HAVERSTICK & CO., photographers.
Cumberland, Allegany Co. (1887). SD.

HELWIG, HOLLI H., photographer.
Pleasant Valley, Garrett Co. (ca. 1890). Imprint on cabinet card, PC.

HEBBEL, J., photographer.
Westminster, Carroll Co. (1887). SD.

HISSONG, J.P., photographer.
Cumberland, Allegany Co. (1866). SD.

HITCHENS, G.W., photographer.
Easton, Talbot Co. (1899-1901). SD.

HOLLINGSWORTH, SAMUEL H., photographer.
Belair, Harford Co. (1899-1901). SD.

HOMER, S.E., photographer.
Belair, Harford Co. (1894-1895). SD.

HOPKINS, CHARLES, photographer.
Annapolis, Anne Arundel Co. (ca. 1866-1871). Imprint on carte de visite, AC, SD.

HOPKINS, JNO. G., photographer.
Annapolis, Anne Arundel Co. (1880). SD.

HUGHES, THOMAS, photographer.
Cokeland, Dorchester Co. (1899-1901). SD.

****

JOHNSON, F. ELMER, photographer.
Easton, Talbot Co. (1891-1892). SD.

JOHNSON, W.R., photographer.
Mountain Lake Park, Garrett Co. (1896-1897). SD.

****

KELLY, HORACE, photographer.
Armacost, Baltimore Co. (1899-1901). SD.

KETTERMAN, GEORGE, photographer.
Highfield, Washington Co. (1891-1892). SD.

KING, WILLIAM D., photographer.
Hagerstown, Washington Co. (1891-1901). SD.

KNIGHT, CHARLES W., photographer.
Main Street, Westminster, Carroll Co. (1880). SD.

KREH, JOHN F., photographer.
Frederick, Frederick Co. (1896-1901). SD.

KRICHTON, J.H., photographer.
Westminster, Carroll Co. (1899-1901). SD.

KUSTER, CHARLES, photographer.
Salisbury, Wicomico Co. (1880). SD.

****

LAMBERT, J.J., photographer.
Frederick, Frederick Co. (1880). SD.

LANEY, VANCE J., photographer.
Cumberland, Allegany Co. (1896-1897). SD.

LARMOUR, ALFRED, photographer.
Sharptown, Wicomico Co. (1871). SD.

LAWSON, T.S., photographer.
Crisfield, Somerset Co. (1880). SD.

LEATHERMAN, JOSIAH, photographer.
Wolfsville, Frederick Co. (1871). SD.

LEE, WILLIAM, photographer.
Port Deposit, Cecil Co. (1866). SD.

LEE, WILLIAM T., photographer.
Havre de Grace, Harford Co. (1866). SD.

LEWIS & MARSHALL, photographers.
Salisbury, Wicomico Co. (1866). SD.

LEWIS, D.S., photographer.
Easton, Talbot Co. (1880-1892). SD.

LEWIS, JOHN S., photographer.
Race St., Cambridge, Dorchester Co. (1871). SD.

LINE, A.A., photographer.
Mountain Lake Park, Garrett Co. (1899-1901). SD.

LINK & LEWIS, photographers.
Easton, Talbot Co. (1887). SD.

LINTON, J.H., itinerant photographer.
Towson, Baltimore Co. (June 1879). BCU, June 21, 1879.

LODER, BENJAMIN, photographer.
Elkton, Cecil Co. (1866). SD.

LOY, JOHN W., photographer.
Loys, Frederick Co. (1891-1901). SD.

LYTLE, J.S., photographer.
Bel Air, Harford Co. (ca. 1870). Imprint on carte de visite, AC.

****

McBRIETY, G.W., photographer.
Salisbury, Wicomico Co. (1880). SD.

McCARTER, WILLIAM, photographer.
Cambridge, Dorchester Co. (ca. 1875). Imprint on CDV, PC.

McKEAN, E.R., photographer.
Elkton, Cecil Co. (1896-1897). SD.

McLAUGHLIN, G.B., photographer.
86 Baltimore, Cumberland, Allegany Co. (1871). SD.

MARKEN & BIELFIELD, photographers.
Frederick, Frederick Co. (1887-1892). SD.

MARKEN & WHITE, photographers.
Over 33 N. Market, Frederick, Frederick Co. (1871). SD.

MARKEN, JOSIAH R., photographer.
Frederick, Frederick Co. (1867-1901). SD.

> The gentleman whose card heads this notice, enjoys the distinction of being the oldest Photographer in Frederick, having established the business in 1860. He is a native Marylander, and like them all, is bountifully gifted with a genial and hospitable disposition. The studio of Mr. Marken is most advantageously located on one of the best corners of the main thoroughfare, and has a remarkably fine skylight, thus giving him the advantages necessary to his work. The reception room shows a handsome display of finished pictures. The studio contains the accessories so important to an artist, and is well managed as to all is details. Not every photographer understands the mechanical portion of the work produces good results. Almost anybody who chooses can master the mere technicalities of the art, and very many do so, and travel about the country making portraits, (so called) whose mechanical effect is a horror to future generations, and ought to be a warning to all who propose to risk themselves in this way. The photographer who is also an artist, who comprehends the niceties of light and shade, understands their proper posing of a sitter, does not tramp about the country lugging his apparatus from town to town, but locates and sticks in one place, and becomes too busy for that sort of thing. Mr. Marken is one of these, hence his steady pursuit for twenty years in this place of his art.... MID.

MARSHALL, J., photographer.
St. Michaels, Talbot Co. (1871). SD.

MARSHALL, JEREMY, photographer.
Wittman, Talbot Co. (1880). SD.

MASLIN, G.L., photographer.
Rockhall, Kent Co. (ca. 1864-1866). Cancelled tax stamps on cartes de visites PC.

MILLER, E.C., photographer.
Havre de Grace, Harford Co. (1891-1895). SD.

MOFFETT, ROBERT O., photographer.
Salisbury, Wicomico Co. (1891-1897). SD.

MORRIS, E.K., photographer.
Easton, Talbot Co. (1896-97). SD.

MORTON, J.R., photographer.
Frederick, Frederick Co. (1866). SD.

MURPHY, MRS. S.M., photographer.
Salisbury, Wicomico Co. (1899-1901). SD.

MYERS, JOSEPH, photographer.
Frostburg, Allegany Co. (1866). SD.

MYERS, THEODORE J., photographer.
Box 27, Pleasant Valley, Garrett Co. (ca. 1875). Imprint on cabinet card, AC.

****

NEIKIRK, FRANK, photographer.
Huyett, Washington Co. (1891-1892). SD.

NEWELL, L.V., photographer.
Point Lookout, St. Mary's Co. (ca. 1864). Imprint on a CDV, AC.

NIMMO, THOMAS J., photographer.
Lonaconing, Allegany Co. (ca. 1870); Main St., Frostburg, Allegany Co. (1875). CDV imprint, PC, PP. (see Baltimore City)

****

O'TOOLE, R., photographer.
Thurmont, Frederick Co. (1899-1901). SD.

****

PAINTER, DAVID F., photographer.
Grave Run Mills, Baltimore Co. (1894-1897). SD.

PALMER, CHARLES H., photographer.
Western Port, Allegany Co. (1891-1892). SD.

PARK, H.A.S., photographer.
No. 40, Baltimore St., Cumberland, Allegany Co. (ca. 1864); & Vanpelt (1866). Imprint on a CDV, PC, SD.

PERKINS, J.W., photographer.
"Successor to Grammer & Perkins, Opp. Odd-Fellows' Hall, Westminster," Carroll Co. (ca. 1870). Imprint on carte de visite, AC.

PERKINS, P.L., photographer.
Hooversville, Anne Arundel Co. (1871). SD. (see Baltimore City)

PHREANER, B.W.T., photographer.
Hagerstown, Washington Co. (1866-1901). SD.

PLUMLEY, H.A., photographer.
Westminster, Carroll Co. (1896-97). SD.

PORTMESS, J.R., photographer.
Cumberland, Allegany Co. (1899-1901). SD.

PRITCHARD, G.H., photographer.
Oakland, Garrett Co. (1887-1897). SD.

PURSOR, SPENCER, photographer.
Leonardtown, St. Mary's Co. (1866). SD.

****

QUIMBY & MIZENER, photographers and jewelers.
Camp Parole, Annapolis, Anne Arundel Co. (ca. 1864). Imprint on carte de visite, AC.

QUINBY & McCLURE, photographers.
Annapolis, Anne Arundel Co. (1866). SD.

****

RAMBO, R.L.C., photographer.
Galena, Kent Co. (1871). SD.

RECHER, ELIAS M., photographer.
Hagerstown, Washington Co. (1866-1887). SD.

REESE, C.S., photographer.
Westminster, Carroll Co. (1887). SD.

REISER, ALOISE, photographer.
Easton, Talbot Co. (1894-97). SD.

RHEA, CHARLES S., photographer.
Cumberland, Allegany Co. (1899-1901). SD.

RICH, H.W., photographer.
16 Main Street, Salisbury, Wicomico Co. (1887). SD.

RICHARDSON, MRS. A.C., photographer.
Fallston, Harford Co. (1899-1901). SD.

ROGERS, A.A., photographer.
Frostburg, Allegany Co. (1880). SD.

ROGERS, W.L., photographer.
Hagerstown, Washington Co. (1887). SD.

ROMER, B.S., photographer.
Belair, Harford Co. (1891-1892). SD.

ROWE, J. & C.F., clothing & photographers.
Emmitsburg, Frederick Co. (1880). SD.

ROWE, JOSHUA, photographer.
Emmitsburg, Frederick Co. (ca. 1864-1866). Cancelled tax stamp on carte de visite, AC.

RYLAND, EDWARD, photographer.
Chestertown, Kent Co. (1866). SD.

****

SCHAEFER, HENRY, photographer.
6 Main Street, Annapolis, Anne Arundel Co. (1888-1895). SD.

SCHLEY, AUTHUR, photographer.
Frederick City, Frederick Co. (1860); $220 capital invested, 1 male employee, $30 average monthly labor cost, 500 photographs produced annually with a $600 value. U.S.M.C. 1860.

SCHWAMB, CHARLES H., photographer.
Annapolis, Anne Arundel Co. (ca. 1864). Imprint on a CDV, PC.

SEELER, WILLIAM W., photographer.
Easton, Talbot Co. (1887). SD.

SHADLE & BUSSER, photographers.
Elkton, Cecil Co. (1894-1895). SD.

SHAW, C.A., photographer.
Nichols, Allegany Co. (1896-1897). SD.

SHAW, H.M., photographer.
Brookeville, Montgomery Co. (1899-1901). SD.

SHUNK, B., photographer.
Sandy Hook, Washington Co. (ca. 1863). Imprint on CDV, PC.

SMETS, HENRY, photographer.
Frostburg, Allegany Co. (1866). SD.

SOUTH, JOHN M., photographer.
Crumpton, Queen Anne's Co. (1891-1892); Chestertown, Kent Co. (1896-1901). SD.

SPARKS, L.W., photographer.
Pocomoke City, Worcester Co. (1899-1901). SD.

SPAULDING, _______________, photographer.
Point Lookout, St. Mary's County (1864). Civil War print, PC.

STEINHARDT, THEO., photographer.
Easton, Talbot Co. (1899-1901). SD.

SWELTZER, CHARLES A., photographer.
Clear Spring, Washington Co. (1871). SD.

****

THOMAS, A. MURRAY, photographer.
Frederick, Frederick Co. (1894-1895). SD.

TILGHMAN, PETER M., photographer.
Crisfield, Somerset Co. (1891-1901). SD.

TOBIAS, HENRY, photographer.
Frederick, Frederick Co. (1866). SD.

TOWLES, CLARENCE O., photographer.
Frostburg and Cumberland, Allegany Co. (1891-1901). SD.

TOWLES, WILLIAM H., photographer.
Cumberland, Allegany Co. (1899-1901). SD.

****

VANDERFORD, ABRAHAM, photographer.
Chestertown, Kent Co. (1871). SD.

VARLEY, CHARLES R., photographer.
Woodwardsville, Anne Arundel Co. (1880). SD.

VARLEY, T.P., photographer.
Woodwardsville, Anne Arundel Co. (1880-1887). SD.

****

WAGONER, JOHN H., photographer.
Boonesboro, Washington Co. (1871); Hagerstown, Washington Co. (1880-1897). SD.

WALSH, EDWARD S., photographer.
East Corner Public Square, Hagerstown, Washington Co. (1866). SD.

WALZL, RICHARD, photographer.
St. Denis, Baltimore Co. (1880). SD. (see Baltimore City)

WAMPLER, JAMES F. & CO., "Photographic Artists."
Chestertown, Kent Co. (ca. 1875). Signed carte de visite, PC. (see Baltimore City)

WASHINGTON FINE ART STUDIO, photographers.
Cumberland, Allegany Co. (1896-97). SD.

WAYS, WILLIAM B., photographer.
Cumberland, Allegany Co. (1891-1892). SD.

WERTZ, H.M., photographer.
Cumberland, Allegany Co. (1899-1901). SD.

WESTON, GEORGE C., photographer.
Pocomoke City, Worcester Co. (ca. 1875). Imprint on cabinet card, AC.

WHITE, J., photographer.
Boonsboro, Washington Co. (ca. 1867). Imprint on CDV, AC.

WHITE, WILLIAM T., photographer.
Waterbury, Anne Arundel Co. (1871). SD.

WILHELMI, F.G., photographer.
Cumberland, Allegany Co. (1871-1880). SD.

WILLIAMS, HUGH J., photographer.
Ludwig, Harford Co. (1891-1901). SD.

WILSON, JOSHUA, photographer.
Mt. Winans, Baltimore Co. (1896-1901). SD.

****

ZULLER, F.M., photographer.
Annapolis, Anne Arundel Co. (1891-1892). SD.

David Bachrach's first Baltimore gallery on the corner of Eutaw and Lexington Streets. Maryland Historical Society Collection

SELECTED BIOGRAPHIES

David Bachrach

The name "Bachrach" has been a hallmark for over 100 years for the oldest photographic studio chain in the United States. Founded in Baltimore, the patriarch of "the first family of photographers" was David Bachrach. The following obituary, which appeared upon his death in 1921, reviewed the character and achievements of one of the leading proponents of photography during its early years.

> "David Bachrach, dean of the portrait photographers of Baltimore, died at 4 o'clock yesterday afternoon at his home, 20 Overhill Road, Roland Park. As a young man he photographed Abraham Lincoln making his Gettysburg address, was war photographer for *Harper's Weekly* during the Civil War, discovered and invented photographic processes that revolutionized the profession of portrait making, and built up a business that achieved an international reputation.
>
> Mr. Bachrach was 76 years old on July 16 last. Since 1914 he had not been actively managing his photographic studios, but seldom missed a day at his office until shortly before his death. He was taken seriously ill last Monday morning, though he spent some time at his Lexington Street studios on the previous Saturday. But heart complications developed, and he grew steadily weaker.
>
> Baltimore knew David Bachrach as a militant publicist, with a gift for strong, intelligent comment on any important public question, almost as well as it knew his professional reputation. He never let an opportunity pass to express an opinion on a subject that he thought vital to the city in which he lived, and his opinions were invariably forceful and authoritative. He had studied Baltimore and its affairs, and he made his voice a powerful influence, usually writing his views to the "Letter Column" of *The Sun*.
>
> Born in Neukirchen, Hesse-Cassel, Germany, July 16, 1845, Mr. Bachrach came to this country when a boy, receiving his education in the public schools of Hartford, Conn. At the age of 15, he took up the study of his life work, apprenticing himself to Robert Vinton Lansdale, a well-known photographer of the early period. After his apprenticeship, he entered the employ of William H. Weaver, then working for *Harper's Weekly*, and embarked upon the career of a war photographer. It was during this connection with *Harper's* that he photographed President Lincoln delivering the address at the dedication of Gettysburg Cemetary.[1]
>
> Then he became assistant photographer at Fort Gilmour [Virginia], and later took charge of the surgical photography at St. John's College Hospital [Annapolis], photographing exchanged

Andersonville prisoners, of whom there were about 1,200 at the hospital. He was offered the rank of a first lieutenant, which he accepted, and was quartered and messed with the officers, though the war ended before his commission papers came through.[2]

In 1866, he was staff photographer for *Leslie's Weekly*, and in 1868 Vice-Admiral Porter appointed him one of the official photographers at the United States Naval Academy.[3] In 1869, he went into business for himself, opening his first studio at the corner of Eutaw and Lexington streets. In November, 1877, he married Miss Fannie Keyser.

Mr. Bachrach was a warm friend of Cardinal Gibbons, who often invited the photographer to walk with him, and called upon him once at his home when he was ill. Every few years, Mr. Bachrach used to get the Cardinal to sit for a portait.

Among his public works was his service on the board which drew up Baltimore's present city Charter. His contributions to the progress in the art of photography were many and valuable, including the invention of photo-engraving of line and stipple subjects, the discovery of a process by which good prints that will not peel may be made on painter's canvas, and the abolishment of the troublesome process of toning chloride of gold. He exposed many widely press-agented humbugs by which photographers were being fooled in the infancy of the profession.

Mr. Bachrach was a member of the Masonic and Odd Fellows orders. He is survived by his wife and three children, Louis Fabian Bachrach of Boston, Mass.; Walter Keyser Bachrach, and Helen Keyser Bachrach, both of Baltimore."[4]

Though the Bachrach's Baltimore studio closed in 1974, the gallery chain still operates in New York, Boston, and several other cities.

David & Daniel Bendann

David and his brother Daniel were born in Richmond, Virginia after their father had emigrated from Prussia in 1832. At the age of sixteen, Daniel began his career in photography when he entered the employment of Jesse Whitehurst's Richmond gallery. While working there, he took the daguerreotype of Edgar Allen Poe that was reproduced as the frontispiece for the *Memorial Volume*, published in Baltimore in 1877. Poe was among the first of many prominent Americans who were eventually captured by the lens of a Bendann. In 1854, Daniel was sent to work in Whitehurst's studio in Baltimore. Once he had become proficient in the art, he returned to Richmond to open his own establishment in 1856.

Two years later, Daniel returned to Baltimore accompanied by his younger brother, David, whom he had introduced to the photographic business as well. During that year of 1858, Daniel worked for the Baltimore and Ohio Railroad, making views along the western line. While in Cumberland, he had the fortune to meet and photograph President Buchanan in his shirt sleeves which resulted in an image that Daniel later said "made an indelible and humorous impression" on his mind.

In 1859, David and Daniel opened their studio at 205 Baltimore Street which soon became one of the leading galleries south of Philadelphia. From that location, they expanded their work in the wet-plate process by offering their clientele the carte de visite style of photograph that was the rage during the 1860's. They were the first to offer this format in the city. David also began to develop his knowledge in fine art which eventually led him to become one of the foremost connoisseurs of his time. As a testament to their skills in the photographic arts, they received a silver medal at the Maryland Institute Fair in 1859 for their retouched photographs in India ink and water color.

With the coming of the Civil War, the Bendanns were quick to take advantage of the public's thirst for images of the prominent personages of the day. They began publishing a series of carte de visite portraits of Southern military and political leaders from negatives that they had made in Virginia before the war. Many of these images were subsequently pirated by other notable photographers that included Mathew Brady, and E. & H.T. Anthony, and C. D. Frederick.

Their sympathies for the Southern cause also led to trouble for both of the brothers. Daniel was arrested in 1862 after an altercation with a Union naval officer which resulted in Bendann's imprisonment. He was finally released after he signed an oath of allegiance to the United States. David was briefly detained by the military authorities in 1865 when he was accused of "disloyal language and keeping at his daguerreotype establishment the negative of likenesses of Rebel Generals." He was released on parole when he pleaded illness and a subsequent search of the studio failed to turn up the alleged negatives.

After the war, the partnership continued to prosper and they expanded by opening an art gallery in 1866 on Fifth Avenue in New York.

Portrait of Daniel (seated) and David (standing) Bendann. Private collection

This was reportedly the first commercial establishment to locate on this prestigious artery. On January 1, 1872, the brothers entered into a brief partnership with the prominent photographer Abraham Bogardus to open a photographic studio in that city. On April 9 of that year, they made a technical contribution to the photographic arts when they patented their ''Improvement in Photographic Backgrounds.'' This enabled photographers to place a new photographic background behind subjects in images by dropping out or replacing the ones originally pictured.

The brothers dissolved their successful partnership in 1874, as each individually pursued his own specialty in Baltimore. Daniel's photographic gallery continued at numerous locations within the city until 1898 as it remained in operation for a few years after his retirement five years earlier. David's fine art gallery continued at 105 Baltimore Street where he offered the work of Whistler, Cameron, Hassam, Bayre, and others to the Baltimore art community. During the early 1900's, he opened another short lived establishment in New York. However, he turned his attention to the rebuilding of the Baltimore gallery with the help of his son, Maurice, after the 1904 fire. Tragically, this location was again struck by another devastating fire in 1982 causing the heirs of David to face the task of relocating their downtown site. The gallery with its suburban outlets continues in operation today still under the ownership of David's family, remaining a living monument to these photographic pioneers.

Daniel died on December 6, 1914 and David followed his older brother with his death on March 20, 1915, less than four months later.[5]

Autographed portrait of Norval Busey. Author's collection

Norval Busey

"Early in life he exhibited quite a taste for pictures, and was never better satisfied then when he was occupied with pencil and paper, making sketches, rather crude is true, but highly satisfactory to himself.

Upon leaving school he was induced by a friend, who was engaged in the photographic business, to learn photography; said friend casually remarking that ANY operator could make $20 per week, and that it would require about THREE MONTHS TO LEARN the business. It is needless to say that this fond DELUSION was dissipated like dew before the morning sun.

After being employed in several different galleries he determined to go west, but while one day passing down Fayette St., in this city, his attention was attracted by the new gallery, just then opened by Messrs. Stanton & Butler. Thinking, perhaps, there might be a chance to rise with a new gallery, he made immediate application for a situation, but was informed that they had no use for more employees. Determined not to give it up, he volunteered his services for NOTHING, and was finally accepted on those terms. (Messrs. Stanton & Butler however, afterwards paid him for all the time he was employed there.) Here he filled several positions, first mounting prints, then printing solar camera prints, finally becoming assistant operator, and upon Mr. Stanton's retiring from the firm, he assumed charge of the operation entirely, and continued in this position until April, 1867, when he purchased a gallery in York, Penna., and there went into business for himself. While there he took the prizes at the country fairs, and soon built up a very excellent business. But wishing for a wider field of action, he entered into co-partnership with O. Hallwig, (who was then transacting business at No. 20 Charles St., in this city,) and removed to Baltimore. This partnership lasted for some eight months, when Mr. Busey opened the large and elegant establishment he now occupies—Mr. Hallwig retaining the old place, which has since burned out. The new gallery of Mr. Busey has been a decided success; his room being constantly crowded by the BON-TON of the city."[6]

Norval H. Busey was born in Christiansburg, Virginia in 1845. He studied art in Paris, France under the tutelage of Bouguereau. The date of his death is currently unknown.

Charles Byerly

"Charles Byerly, proprietor of the well-known and long established art and photograph gallery that was founded nearly seventy-five years ago in Frederick City, Md., was born in that city, January 24, 1874. He is a son of John Davis and Mary (Markell) Byerly.

Jacob Byerly, the grandfather of Charles Byerly, a son of Henry Byerly, was a native of Pennsylvania, and descended of an old German family of that State. Jacob Byerly was also a native of Pennsylvania, and in 1842 removed to Frederick City, where he died in 1881. He engaged in the making of daguerreotypes, the forerunners of modern photography. He established the business that is now conducted by his grandson, Charles Byerly. He met with success in the undertaking, and was one of the leading citizens of Frederick in his time. He was held in high esteem by all who knew him. He was married to Catharine Bear, daughter of David Bear, of Cumberland County, Pa.

John Davis Byerly, the father of Charles Byerly, son of Catharine (Bear) Byerly, was born in Newville, Cumberland County, Pa., in 1839. He came to Frederick with his parents, where he learned the trade of a photographer under his father, and for many years conducted the business now owned by his son, Charles Byerly. He met with substantial success, and in 1899 retired from active business cares. He is one of the leading and best known citizens of Frederick. In politics, he has always been an adherent of the Republican party. Fraternally, he is a member of the Order of Red Men. He is affiliated in a religious way with Grace Reformed Church of Frederick, of which he is an active and consistent member. Mr. Byerly was married in 1869, to Mary Markell, daughter of George Markell, who was a prominent merchant of Frederick. She is also a member of Grace Reformed Church. They were the parents of four children, two of whom survive: Charles and Mary Catharine, the wife of Thomas A. Chapline.

Charles Byerly, son of John Davis and Mary (Markell) Byerly, received his education in the public schools of Frederick and at the Frederick City Academy. He learned the trade of his father and grandfather, that of a photographer, and was associated in that business with his father until 1899, when he became the proprietor of the business, which he has since conducted. This gallery is located in North Market Street, and was founded nearly three quarters of a century ago by the grandfather of the present owner. He has met with substantial success in the undertaking, and his establishment is one of the leading photograph galleries of the city. He is well known, and is highly esteemed by all who know him.

In politics, Mr. Byerly is a member of the Republican party. He is allied in a religious way with the Lutheran Church. He is also a member of the Frederick City Lodge, No. 684, Benevolent and Protective Order of Elks. Mr. Byerly was married in 1902, to Regina Eisenhaur, daughter of John Eisenhaur, a well-known merchant of Frederick City. Mr. and Mrs. Byerly are the parents of two sons, John F. and Charles." [7]

John Holyland

"Holyland, John, was born at Harsimus, Jersey City, October 6, 1841. His parents were natives of England, who emigrated to the United States about the year 1830. His father was an engraver, and acquired such skill in the art, that, within a few years after commencing business on his own account, he accumulated considerable wealth. Owing, however, to an ill-advised real estate transaction and some disastrous shipping ventures, it was entirely swept away. Soon after their arrival in this country, his parents unified with the Baptist Church; and so in after-life, gave bent to their son's religious views and denominational preferences. After many vicissitudes, the family residence was established in Baltimore, where they were living at the breaking out of the war of 1861. At the age of nineteen, John Holyland, the subject of this sketch, turned his attention to the study of photography. He entered the photographic gallery of Mr. Young, on the southwest corner of Baltimore and Charles Streets, Baltimore, and assiduously applied himself to an acquisition of art. While as yet he had attained but a limited knowledge of the business, his father purchased a gallery in Washington, District of Columbia, and placed him in charge of it. An average inexperienced youth would have been utterly discouraged and led to abandon the undertaking in dispair; but the difficulties to be surmounted served to give new zest to his pursuits of the requisite knowledge to constitute him a skillful artist. Through the day, and far into the night, he experimented and toiled, until at last success crowned his efforts. At the age of twenty-four years, he married his cousin Miss Rebecca Hart, of Middletown, Orange County, New York, July 27, 1865. On the death of his father, which occurred three months after his marriage he returned to Baltimore and commenced business in the same gallery where he took his first lesson in photography. Mr. Holyland has met with great success and achieved a fine reputation as an artist. In recognition of his merits, he has been chosen Vice-President for the State of Maryland, of the National Photographic Society. He is a member of the Franklin Square Baptist Church, a very successful teacher of a young men's Bible class in the Sunday school of that church, and is actively and heartily engaged in mission work, under the auspices of the denomination to which he belongs."[8]

Holyland died in Baltimore on May 19, 1931.

B. W. T. Phreaner

"B. W. T. Phreaner, a leading photographer of Hagerstown, was born in Cearfoss District, No. 13, October 9, 1845, son of William and Louisiana (Bowman) Phreaner, both now deceased.

William Phreaner was a tailor by trade and was born in Lebanon County, Pa., May 19, 1819. He was the son of John Phreaner, who died when his son William was only four years of age. William Phreaner died in Washington County in 1839. John Phreaner, great-grandfather of B. W. T. Phreaner, emigrated from the German Palatinate, and settled in Lancaster, now Lebanon County, Pa., among the early German emigrants. He was the father of a large family.

B. W. T. Phreaner was the only son of William Phreaner and was but six years old when his parents removed to Hagerstown, where he grew to manhood, and received his education in the public schools. At the age of fifteen he began the study of photography. In 1864 he engaged in business for himself, which he has continued successfully for the past forty-two years. In later years, Mr. Phreaner has given much attention to outdoor and landscape photography, and has practiced his art in all its branches. He has made a high reputation for outdoor, as well as portrait work.

Mr. Phreaner married, in February, 1869, Miss Emma C. Wagner, daughter of Samuel and Catherine Wagner, of the vicinity of Keedysville, Washington County. Mr. Wagner was a successful farmer; he died in 1892, aged ninety years. Mr. and Mrs. Phreaner were the parents of six children: Lulie, who is the wife of George E. Stover, of Hagerstown; they have a daughter Helen; Will, died in childhood; Edith, unmarried, of Hagerstown; Leighton K., of Hagerstown; Edgar C., of Hagerstown; and Franklin, of Hagerstown.

In politics, Mr. Phreaner is a strong Prohibitionist, and has been an active worker in the cause of Prohibition for the past twenty years. He is an active member of Christ's Reformed Church of Hagerstown. He is also a member of the Ancient Order of United Workman.

Mrs. Phreaner's mother, whose maiden name was Mumma, was a descendant of the early families of Washington County. Of her brothers and sisters, the following survive: John H., Samuel and Benjamin, of Boonsboro, Md., and Mrs. H. B. Snively."[9]

Henry Pollock

Henry Pollock was the most enduring of Baltimore's pioneer photographers whose career spanned the era of the daguerreotype through the end of the wet-plate process in the 1880's. Little is known, however, about this man whose work was often noted for its quality of execution, placing him among the recognized artists of his day.

Pollock was born in Washington, D. C. in 1810. Most of his early life remains a mystery except that he was initially employed in woodworking. Though it is not known when he took up daguerreotyping, he was sufficiently proficient in the art by 1848 to offer instruction to others. Isaac Briggs, an itinerant Maryland daguerrean, mentions in his journal that he "commenced learning Daguerreotyping from Mr. Pollock [on] April 25th, 1848" for which he paid a tuition of $25.00. By 1849, Pollock had established his first gallery at 147 Lexington Street, followed by his relocation to 155 Baltimore Street the following year.

During his years of working with the daguerreotype, Pollock advertised frequently in the local press and was often active in affairs that affected the fraternity. He was part of a group of daguerreans that petitioned the city for permission to display their work in showcases on the sidewalk in front of their galleries. It is unclear if he was a participant in the 1855 attempt to organize a local daguerrean association. However, he did join the National Photographic Association by 1869.

Pollock's studio was reviewed numerous times in local newspapers and national trade journals and it is through these that more can be learned about the man and his business. *The Photographic and Fine Art Journal* reported in 1857 that:

> Mr. Pollock has his gallery in the best location in Baltimore probably; his apartments are of the best; no gallery in the country is superior, and yet he is not kept busy. You can always get a good picture at Mr. P.'s gallery, and everything that he does is of the best possible kind. His daguerreotypes and ambrotypes are good, his photographs are good also. But Mr. Pollock lacks the blarney which all operators generally have; and if he had a little more of the Young America in him, he would do the best business in Baltimore. Mr. P. does a small business but a safe one, and manages to do a paying business. Mr. P. is a conscientious, straight-forward, steady, upright man.[10]

A short time later, they again commented upon his operation:

> Mr. Pollock has probably one of the most elegant galleries in Baltimore. But Mr. Pollock belongs to the old school and has very little flattery, and often loses a picture where he might have secured one by a little soft talk . . . Mr. Pollock has the most complete operating and chemical rooms in Baltimore; he does his own operating; business is dull . . .[11]

Robert E. Lee by Henry Pollock. This previously unpublished photograph may well be the last portrait of Lee before his death in 1870. Author's collection

Henry Pollock

In light of this reported lack of rapport with his patrons, Isaac Briggs recounted Pollock's own philosophy about dealing with customers:

> As the operator is always held responsible for the position and attitudes as well as the resemblance of his pictures to their originals and as bad attitudes with people of taste are incompatible with good likenesses, he should control and make the most of the former and if the Daguerreotype be good and properly timed, the latter will come as a matter of course.[12]

By the end of 1856, Pollock had adapted the new technology of the wet-plate process and added the ambrotype and paper photographs to his trade. As the carte de visite and the cabinet card formats came into vogue, he adopted them as well. Though sensitive to the latest deveopments and fashions in the art, Pollock still seemed to lack the spirit of "Young America," preferring to conduct a modest business with few employees. However, he remained in business until 1889 and had among his clientele many of the notables of the day. Thus, Henry Pollock's legacy is primarily seen today through the large amount of his work that has endured.

Portrait of William Shorey from The Biographical Cyclopedia of Representative Men of Maryland and District of Columibia, *1879.*

William F. Shorey

"Shorey, William Foss, Artist and Photographer, was born April 20, 1833, at Hollis, Maine. His parents were Nehemiah B. and Ann (Chase) Shorey, both of whom were natives of Massachusetts, the former being of English descent, and latter of French-English extraction. His mother was daughter of the Rev. Joshua Chase, of Massachusetts. Mr. Shorey's parents removed to Baltimore about the year 1840.

His father was for many years engaged in merchandising and milling in Maine, and was held in high esteem by the citizens of Hollis and vicinity on account of his strict integrity and benevolence. He was a man of great energy and perseverance, which traits of character being recognized by an American ship company, a proposition was made to him, in 1835, to undertake the contract of building two ships, to be delivered at the mouth of the Saco River. The distance, some eight miles inland (where the timber needed was plentiful), deterred all others from undertaking so difficult a task. Accepting the contract, he completed the vessels, launched them when the river was swollen, and floated them about four miles to a dam, around which, with over a hundred yoke of oxen, he hauled the vessels, re-launched them, and floated them, without accident, to the place designated.

After receiving a common-school education, the subject of this sketch served an apprenticeship of five years at the tinner's trade, and soon after attaining his majority was employed in the tinning department of Mr. C. S. Maltby's packing establishment, during which time he attended the evening sessions of the School of Design of the Maryland Institute. Here a strong talent for art was developed, and in connection with drawing, he pursued the studies of oil painting and photography. After graduating with honor, taking on of the Peabody premiums, he became, and was for a number of years, teacher of the elementary class of drawing at the Institute. He selected photography as the branch of art best suited to his inclinations, and withdrew from the employment of Mr. Maltby, to establish himself in business in Baltimore. He first located at No. 87 West Baltimore Street, and after remaining there, and at No. 105, same street, for a number of years, he removed to No. 157 West Baltimore Street, where he is still in business.

He has had a successful career and his success is mainly attributed to the fact that he has always been conscientious in the execution of his work, exerting himself to the utmost to give satisfaction, and availing himself of the latest inventions and improvements in the art, so as to keep pace with the demands of the business. His skill as an artist has won him an enviable reputation, and by diligence, energy, and strict integrity, he has succeeded in building up a lucrative business.

He is President of the Maryland Wool Company, having its headquarters at Canton, organized several years ago for the purpose of extracting wool from delain rags by a new chemical process. He has been a Freemason for the past ten years; he is a member of the Odd Fellows, and has held the principal offices in a subordinate lodge of that order; and is also a member

Photograph gallery of William Shorey at 157 W. Baltimore Street. Standing on the second floor ledge is William M. Chase (left) and Shorey (right). Author's collection

of the Knights of the Golden Eagle, a mutual benefit order, which he helped to organize in Baltimore in 1873, the first meetings for the purpose of the organization having been held in Mr. Shorey's gallery. This order now has about a thousand members in Baltimore, and is steadily increasing in numbers and influence in various parts of the country.''[13]

Portrait of John H. Walzl from The Biographical Cyclopedia of Representative Men of Maryland and District of Columbia, 1879.

John Henry Walzl

"Walzl, John Henry, was born, June 23, 1833, in Stein, on the Danube, Lower Austria. He received a thorough education at the University of Krems, near the above city, in which he was a student for about seven years, and graduated at the age of sixteen years. While at college he found time to make himself conversant with the trade pursued by his father, that of jeweler. His collegiate and business education completed he went to St. Poelten, near Vienna, and subsequently to the Austrian Capital, where he engaged in the jewelry business. After remaining in the latter city for about a year he obtained a permit from the Imperial Government to travel beyond the confines of Austria. He made a general European tour, and then established himself in his vocation in Geneva, Switzerland. He left Geneva and went to Winterthur, where he received a summons from the authorities of the Austrian government to return home and enter its military service. This he disregarded, and immediately turned his course toward America. He set sail from the port of Havre, France, and in September of 1853 landed in New York. He obtained a situation in the jewelry establishment of David Raith, and subsequently in the house of Tiffany, Young & Ellis, where he earned as high as forty dollars a week in simply setting diamonds, in which he was quite an expert. He remained in New York two years, during which time he saved enough to provide for his family a home in Hoboken, where he had purchased several building lots.

Being compelled to change his business on account of impaired health he removed to Baltimore, Maryland, and in 1854 associated with him Mr. Beeckman Cooke in the daguerreotype business, under the firm style of Cooke & Walzl. Six months after the copartnership was formed Mr. Walzl bought the entire interest of the establishment. He extended his business considerably, engaging largely in the supplying of daguerreotype stock or material to the Southern trade. Upon the introduction of photography in 1856 he again expanded his business, his establishment becoming the leading one of its kind in Baltimore. Mr. Walzl was the inventor of Tatum's Patent Oilground Photographs, a process whereby photographs can be printed directly on the oiled canvas.

Since 1868 Mr. Walzl has devoted himself very extensively to operations in real estate. Waverly, on York Road, Baltimore County, owes its origin and growth largely to him. As early as 1860 he purchased considerable land in that place, and has erected thereon many elegant and valuable structures. He also purchased Chancellorsville, Virginia, which was the scene of bloody conflicts during the Civil War. This tract of land embraced about one thousand acres. The old Chancellor Hotel, which was destroyed during the war, was renovated by him; he built a schoolhouse, and established a flourishing Sunday school, Mr. P. R. Uhler, Librarian of the Peabody Institute, kindly furnishing the books and exerting in behalf of the religious work. Mr. Walzl's aim was to colonize the above section of Virginia with industrious Germans, who would develop its resources and thus add largely to the substantial wealth and prosperity of the State. Through his instrumentality three hundred Germans were brought from their native country and located at Chancellorsville. His enterprise attracted the attention of the Governor of Virginia, and Mr. Walzl was invited by him, in letters dated January 8, 1871, and January 18, 1872, to address the Committee on Immigration of the State Senate of Virginia at Richmond in reference to the results of his colonization operations and his views on the same, which he did in proper terms eliciting the approval of the entire State Legislature. The late Archbishop Spaulding, Bishop of Baltimore, addressed a letter to the late Bishop McGill of Richmond requesting him to forward Mr. Walzl's projects in the colonizing emigrants. Mr. Walzl's operations in Virginia extended from 1870 to 1873, when he returned to his home in Waverly. Subsequently he and his wife made a prolonged tour of Europe, revisiting the scenes of his childhood on the shores of the Danube.

Mr. Walzl married in 1857 Miss Augusta Eisenbrandt, daughter of Christian H. Eisenbrandt, a well-known musical instrument manufacturer of Baltimore. He was a native of Gottigen, Germany, and came to America in 1812. Mrs. Walzl died in 1877. Three children survive her: John Henry, Sidney and Elenora. Mr. Walzl married, a second time, August 22, 1878, Miss Benjamin and Mary Ann Horn. Mr. Horn is a wealthy and influential citizen of Baltimore County."[14]

Richard Walzl

"Walzl, Richard Edmund, was born, October 14, 1843, in Stein, Austria. His father, John Walzl, was a highly respectable citizen of that place, and a manufacturer of gold and silver ware. He possessed an original and ingenious mind, and was widely known for his integrity and purity of character. At the conclusion of the revolution in Austria in 1848, he was selected as a delegate from Stein for signing the declaration of peace between the Emperor and the people. He held rank of military commander, and was for some time a burgomaster of his native town.

In 1852 he came with his family to America, and settled in Baltimore. He placed Richard at Professor Knapp's Institute, where he remained two years, and then began the study of the art of photography. At the expiration of four years he commenced the photographic business on his own account in Harford County, Maryland where he saved in a year or so sufficient to enable him to open a photographic establishment in Baltimore, at 77 West Baltimore Street, in 1862. He pursued his business successfully in that locality for five years, when he moved into the fine marble building, No. 103 West Baltimore Street, constructed especially for his business. In 1872 he removed to 46 North Charles Street, where he is now located.

It has been the aim of Mr. Walzl to place his art at the highest point of perfection, and with this view he has adopted every new and ingenious process that his own inventive mind or that of other masters of his profession have suggested. Prior to opening his studio, Mr. Walzl made an extensive tour through the United States and the Canadas, visiting the leading photographic art establishments in the principal cities. He was thus enabled to introduce many new features into his own. He is the editor and publisher of the *Photographic Rays of Light*, a popular photographic magazine. He also issues *The Photographer's Friend*, which is devoted to the financial and commercial interests of photography. In 1878 he issued a publication containing full instructions and advice to sitters as to their dress, position, time for sitting, expressions, etc., and a complete description of the photographic art. The book also embraces a history of the origin and progress of photography. In this publication he endeavors to cultivate a high appreciation of the beautiful and a sympathy with art, an aesthetic taste and elevated sentiments in regard to the pictures of cherished friends or relatives. He competed with some of the best artists of the country at a fair of the Maryland Institute, and carried off the premium for plain photographs. The porcelain miniatures executed at Mr. Walzl's establishment have secured a special medal of merit on account of their exquisite delicacy in finish and permanency.

Commencing with scarcely a dollar, Mr. Walzl has, by his own exertions and talents, achieved great success. He is highly esteemed for his superior intelligence, his sensitive appreciation of all that is good and beautiful, and for his strict integrity. In June, 1874, Mr. Walzl married Miss Henrietta E. Scheib, third daughter of Rev. Henry Scheib, of Baltimore. He has two children, Aimee and Richard." [15]

Richard Walzl died in Baltimore on May 10, 1899.

Juried exhibit displaying photographs from Richard Walzl's gallery. Author's collection

Jesse Whitehurst

Jesse H. Whitehurst was one of photography's leading practitioners and entrepreneurs during the medium's first twenty-five years. From his Baltimore residence, the Virginia native presided over a chain of galleries that stretched from New York to the Carolinas. His work won both local and international acclaim. As a leader in artistic and technical advances, Whitehurst sought out the most skilled operators and colorists to maintain his standard of excellence. Recognizing the power of the press, he used innovative advertising to promote his studios and capitalized on the public's demand for images of the newsmakers of the day. The following period biography recounts some of his achievements:

> If we have been informed aright, Jesse H. Whitehurst is the son of Captain Charles Whitehurst, one of the gallant heroes of Craney Island, and was born in Priness Anne County, Virginia. He is still young, of prepossessing appearance, and urbane manners. At an early age, he evinced great mechanical and artistical talent, coupled with enterprise and ambition. In 1843, the art of Daguerreotyping might have been considered in its infancy; he had foresight enough to see that there was a wide field opened before him. He accordingly visited New York — gleaned what information he could, and, through books and study, obtained knowledge enough of the art to commence for himself — which he did successfully in Charleston, S.C. In the fall of 1843, he opened a gallery in Norfolk, and such was his success that, with his usual 'go-ahead-ativeness' in January of 1844, he established his celebrated gallery in Richmond. Good fortune still smiled upon his exertions; and such was his triumph over all competition, that he successively opened his branch establishments in Lynchburg, Petersburg, Baltimore, and New York. In 1844, he discovered the rotatory background, an improvement which gives an airy, life-like appearance to the picture. In 1845, he constructed the first perfect skylight in Richmond; this improvement diffuses pleasant and equal light over the countenance of the sitter, and consequently greatly improves the picture. In 1846, he applied galvanism to Daguerreotypes, and by a series of successful experiments proved its utility, when all others failed in its application. To give the reader some idea of the amount of business done by this enterprising young artist, something over 60,000 pictures were sent out from his establishment during the six years that transpired after he first commenced business, giving employment to twenty-three assistants.
>
> "He seldom, if ever gives dissatisfaction, and never allows a defective picture to leave his gallery. This is the main secret of great success; for every one being pleased, recommendations must come from every quarter. His success in Baltimore has been unprecendented — benefitting him, while, at the same time, it throws business into

Jesse Whitehurst was among the many photographers that located a gallery at 213 Baltimore Street, over the store of J. E. Bird & Bro's. Note the skylight structure on the roof. Author's collection

the hands of his competitors, who are numerous, and some of them extremely skillful. The high finish and rich tones of his pictures have put everybody in mind of having their likeness taken; and this newly-created desire does not confine the patronage of the public to him alone, but distributes it among those who have real merit."

At one of the fairs of the Maryland Institute, held in Baltimore, he was awarded the first premium for the superiority of his pictures.

"The English journals, particularly the 'Illustrated London News,' were enthusiastic in their praise of Whitehurst's Daguerreotype views of Niagra Falls, exhibited in the Crystal Palace. These views are perfect gems of art, and conveyed a more correct idea of this great natural wonder of the world than our transatlantic friends have ever had before."

The mind of Whitehurst is one of rare and varied inventive capacity; and it would be difficult to conjecture in what direction his genius may hereafter tend, or what further results may be developed by his skill in his favourite art.[16]

Though not a native of Baltimore, Whitehurst found a home in the city in which he helped establish as a center of the photographic arts. He died here on September 8, 1875.

DO YOUR OWN SOLAR PRINTING.

THE ONLY AWARD
by the
CENTENNIAL COMMISSION
to any Apparatus for Making
Enlarged Photographs directly from smaller negatives.

PATENTED
Feb. 24, 1857.
July 10, 1866.
Feb. 23, 1871.
May 26, 1874.
Aug. 4, 1874.

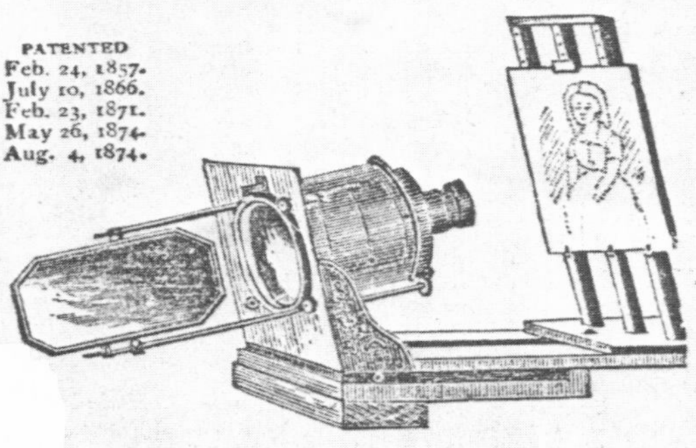

Reflecting and Direct Printing

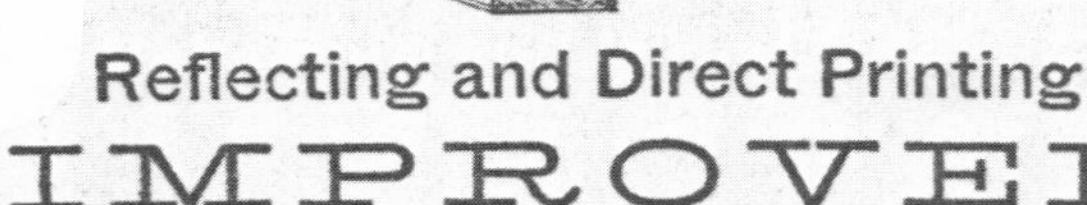

SOLAR CAMERAS,

Manufactured at Baltimore by D. A. WOODWARD, the original inventor and patentee of Solar Cameras, combining the latest improvements.

Prices of DIRECT PRINTING *and* REFLECTING SOLAR CAMERAS:

18 inch diameter condensing lens, will print	40 x 50 inch, . .	$400 00,	Boxing, $8 00
15 " " " " "	29 x 36 " . .	275 00,	" 6 00
12 " " " " "	25 x 30 " . .	220 00,	" 4 00
10 " " " " "	18 x 23 " . .	190 00,	" 2 50
5 " " " " "	*Reflecting only,* .	60 00,	" 1 50

The 5 inch condensing lens camera is intended more especially for TRACING by ARTISTS IN OIL, CRAYONS, PASTEL, etc., and is also recommended as a valuable adjunct to the PHOTOGRAPHIC GALLERY, where it is desirable to make enlargements by any process of development.

Any of the REFLECTING CAMERAS may be made to print much larger than the above marked sizes by increasing the distance of the easel from the Camera.

Every Camera will be tested and guaranteed before delivery, and will be licensed and accompanied by the regular PATENT STAMP of the patentee. Can be ordered through any STOCK DEALER or directly from either of the undersigned.

D. A. WOODWARD, Maryland Institute, BALTIMORE.

E. & H. T. ANTHONY & CO., Manufacturer's Agents, NEW YORK.

☞ *All persons are Cautioned against Infringing the Solar Camera Patents.* ☜

Advertisement for David Woodward's solar camera from Anthony's Photographic Bulletin, *April 1877. Author's collection*

David A. Woodward

"Woodward, David Acheson, Professor of Fine Arts, was born in Philadelphia, Pa., September 16, 1823. His grandfather was W. W. Woodward, a well-known publisher of Philadelphia. His father was William Hill Woodward, who, after carrying on the publishing business for some time in Philadelphia, removed, with his family to Cincinnati, O. Here he established the first, and at that time the only publishing house in Cincinnati, which business he carried on there successfully for several years. His mother was Eliza Young, only child by first marriage of David Acheson, of Washington, Pa., a prominent politician and member of Congress, and a native of the North of Ireland, and descendant in the collateral branch of the family of Archibald Acheson, Lord Gosford, in the Peerage of Ireland, and ex-Governor General of Canada.

In Cincinnati, David very soon began to show a liking and aptness for art. When not more than five or six years old, he began to draw in imitation of other drawings and paintings. Before he was ten years of age, he began to draw and paint from nature. His first painting in oil, a portrait of his brother, was made at about the age of fifteen. His mind was so much taken up with art, that his father found it difficult to have him give attention to anything else. When about thirteen years of age, he went to college at Washington, Pa., for about three years. He then returned to Cincinnati, and, in connection with T. Buchanan Read, who was then painting, opened a studio. After painting in Cincinnati for about a year, he went to Philadelphia, opened a studio on Chestnut Street, and also continued the study of painting and drawing from the casts in the Pennsylvania Academy. After remaining there for about two years, he left the city, and for four years travelled and painted. In this way he travelled over a great part of the United States.

In the fall of 1847 he located in Baltimore, Maryland, and occupied for a number of years a studio on the corner of North and Fayette Streets. In 1851 he married Miss Josephine, only daughter of Joseph Laty, a well-known shipbuilder of Baltimore, From this union he has now living five sons and two daughters. Mary, a highly educated and interesting girl died in 1876, at the age of twenty-one. In 1852 he was engaged by the Maryland Institute, which has been but recently organized, as Instructor of Drawing. In 1853 he was elected as principal of the department, which position he held until 1860, when he was elected by the board to reorganize the school, which resulted in the present School of Art and Design, and of which he was chosen principal. This position he has ever since held. The success of this school has been unparalleled in this country. The report of the United States Commissioner, at Washington, shows that the school in 1874 and 1875 had twelve teachers and a yearly attendance of five hundred students.

Mr. Woodward has also been ingenious in inventions, the most important of which is the solar camera. It is the apparatus by which all large photographs are made, and is now in common use. In 1859 he visited Europe, where he successfully introduced the camera. This invention brought about an entire revolution in photography. Professor Woodward has painted the life-size portraits of many of the most eminent men of the last half century."[17]

BIOGRAPHICAL NOTES

1. Though credited with photographing Lincoln while he delivered his famous address, Bachrach was unclear in his memoirs as to whether or not he actually made any negatives during those brief moments.

2. These photographs were later used as evidence in the war crimes trial of the camp commandant, Henry Wirz.

3. Bachrach operated this studio with William M. Chase, with whom he had begun working soon after the end of the Civil War.

4. *The Sun*, December 11, 1921.

5. Daniel Bendann, "The Memories of a Veteran Baltimore Photographer," *The Sunday Sun*, November 8, 1908, p. 17; Felix Bendann, "Bendann Art Galleries," February 1977, Pratt Library, Baltimore, Md.

6. Richard Walzl, "Norval H. Busey," *The Photographer's Friend*, April 1871, pp. 58-59.

7. Thomas J.C. Williams, *History of Frederick County* (L.R. Titsworth & Co., 1910), pp. 927-928.

8. *The Biographical Cyclopedia of Representative Men of Maryland and District of Columbia* (Baltimore: National Biographical Publishing Co., 1879), p. 222.

9. Thomas J.C. Williams, *A History of Washington County* (John M. Runk & L.R. Titsworth, 1906), p. 1210.

10. *The Photographic and Fine Art Journal* 10 (September 1857): 263.

11. Ibid., (August 1857): 252.

12. Isaac Briggs Daguerrean Journal, Briggs Collection, MS 147, Box 3B, Maryland Historical Society, Baltimore, Maryland.

13. *Biographical Cyclopedia of Representative Men*, p. 221.

14. Ibid., pp. 684-685.

15. Ibid., pp. 392-393.

16. William S. Forrest, *Historical and Descriptive Sketches of Norfolk and Vicinity* (Philadelphia: Lindsay and Blakiston, 1853), pp. 397-398.

17. *Biographical Cyclopedia of Representative Men*, p. 158.